D0273826

NHS Mergers, Management and Mayhem

101 Questions for Managers

Roy Lilley and Eve Richardson

THE INSTITUTE OF
HEALTH SERVICES
MANAGEMENT

Better Management • Better Health

Published in association with
The Institute of Health Services Management

KOGAN
PAGE

YOURS TO HAVE AND TO HOLD

BUT NOT TO COPY

First published in 1998

Apart from any fair dealing for the purposes of research or private study, or criticism or review, as permitted under the Copyright, Designs and Patents Act 1988, this publication may only be reproduced, stored or transmitted, in any form or by any means, with the prior permission in writing of the publishers, or in the case of reprographic reproduction in accordance with the terms of licences issued by the Copyright Licensing Agency. Enquiries concerning reproduction outside those terms should be sent to the publishers at the under-mentioned address:

Kogan Page Limited
120 Pentonville Road
London N1 9JN

British Library Cataloguing in Publication Data
A CIP record for this book is available from the British Library.
ISBN 0 7494 2613 6

Typeset by Kogan Page
Printed and bound in Great Britain by Clays Ltd, St Ives plc

Contents

Preface

Eve Richardson and Roy Lilley are well qualified to write a book about merging NHS Trusts; the pitfalls, the consequences, the challenges and the delights.

They've been there, done it, bought the T-shirt and have now written the book.

As chief executive and chairman, they merged the Homewood NHS Trust with their neighbouring community-based Trust, Weybourne.

They made the decision to merge to improve services and for no other reason.

They believe you shouldn't either.

Many people have been curious about what it was like to work at the famous Homewood NHS Trust.

In recent times, understandably, there has been particular interest to know about the merger between Homewood and its neighbour Weybourne.

This book is by way of explanation; a guide and an apology to all the people to whom Eve Richardson and Roy Lilley promised to tell their story and send copies of presentations about their merger, and have now mislaid a business card or just forgot!

This book is dedicated to the board members, managers and staff who gave birth to the Bournewood NHS Trust.

This book is not just about questions; it is mainly about answers. Or, at least, thinking about and finding the answers.

Modern healthcare poses many questions for the clinicians, managers and boards, who together have the ultimate responsibility for *making it happen* for patients, residents, clients and their relatives, carers and friends.

Knowing which questions to ask is the first step. Not all the quoteuestions in this book are board-level strategic and complex ones. Some are basic, mundane and managerial.

Our book is not a trap and is not designed to make you look a fool if you don't know the answers. If you believe, as we believe, that it is the quest for the answers that is important, then you share our goal – to run organisations more effectively.

If an organisation is ready to acknowledge it does not have all the answers and is brave enough to look for them, then this book will stop being just a list of questions and will become a signpost, a compass, and a route map into the future.

This book comes at a time when the future of the NHS is undergoing more change. The recently published white paper, with the intriguing sub-title 'Breathing New Life into the NHS' will encourage some and disappoint others. One subtle change that is heralded, in the jargon of the NHS, is the possebility of the unification of the GMS and HCHS budgets. In English that means the General Medical Services Budget and the Hospital and Community Health Budgets will be merged and run as one. Explosive stuff.

The transfer, interchange and merging of primary and secondary care budgets could mean the transfer, interchange and merging of primary and secondary care services. As the NHS ebbs and flows, changes and reconfiguration will follow in their wake. Secondary services might be forced to face a more uncertain future than they think: slimmer. Primary care services may become plumper and more integrated and definitely more complex.

More mergers, tougher management and a lot more mayhem.

Good luck.

Eve Richardson
Roy Lilley

Part 1

Why Mergers?

1
The Background

It was back in 1993 that the NHS first got interested in the prospect of mergers. At the time the service was gripped by the language of the market. NHS managers, many of whom had been trapped for years in a suffocating bureaucracy, hoped that an infusion of private sector practice would revolutionise their work.

At one point, the then Secretary of State for Health was moved to warn Regional Health Authorities, the Department of Health and others to 'get your tanks off the Trust's lawns'. This powerful metaphor was used by Virginia Bottomley, to great effect. Trusts, still in their development phase, were feeling their way and needed space to grow and deliver.

As fast as managers on the ground were trying to turn patients into people with the rights of customers, and to fulfil the expectations entitled to a paying public, managers at the centre were worried that a too-ferocious embrace of a 'market' economy in the health services, without proper planning and guidance, would be the kiss of death and the collapse of the whole system.

The duplication of services, and the horrible costs of running a paper driven administration that had too much redundant capital infrastructure for a service that was about to halve its bed usage, were producing intolerable pressures.

Non-executive newcomers to the NHS who had a business background, and also many NHS managers, knew the answer was to close some hospitals and use the money to bolster and improve services in a concentrated form. The language of closure was too much for the civil servants and the politicians. Politicians had learned, long ago – you close a hospital at your peril. So, a new word was borrowed from the language of business: *merger*. Merger was the big idea. To save money, downsize services in a way that the public were not supposed to notice – merger was seized upon as the answer to the problems of the NHS back in the early 1990s.

This book is about the thoughts and experiences of both of us, with something Roy came across while on a research trip to the USA. Spending a few days looking at Wall Street, the markets and how they really worked started to shape his thinking about mergers. In one of the dealing rooms, crowded

3

with computer screens and a community of dervishes all screaming at each other, he came across a card pinned to a notice board in a quiet corner. It said 'Two Turkeys Don't Make an Eagle'.

He loved the language and used it as a centre-piece for his monthly column in the health managers' magazine *Healthcare Today*.
This is what he said...

Two turkeys don't make an eagle

Reproduced by kind permission of the editor, *Heathcare Today.*

Two wrongs don't make a right. Two swallows don't make a summer. I do love English aphorisms. Only the Americans do them better. I have collected a new one: 'Two turkeys don't make an eagle'. In idiomatic American/English a turkey is a dunce, a nitwit. A turkey flaps around, growing plump, preparing for his appointment with the Thanksgiving (or, in our case, the Christmas) carving knife. He hasn't got the brains to understand that slim turkeys live longer.

In the language of Wall Street, this aphorism means putting two businesses together does not guarantee a better business will result. In the words of the market analyst and business guru, Michael Porter: 'Mergers are a drug that makes managers feel good in the short term but saps the energy of the organisation in the long run.'

As the NHS strives for greater efficiency through businesslike practices, the language of enterprise is part of the lexicon of health care. Before we are all mesmerised by merger mania, we might do well to have a look at what mergers have done for businesses.

In the McKinsey Study of US mergers, from 1972–83 only 23% were successful. What is the definition of success? – increased dividends for shareholders. The mid-1980s saw a hectic round of mergers in boardrooms all over Europe. The parallels between business and health are irresistible. The changing economic and trading environments and shifts in technological achievement are forcing the pace of change in business and in health.

Business Week, August 17 1992, reported: 'The average bank merger in the 1980s didn't cut costs, didn't raise productivity and actually made the combined bank less profitable.' What are the lessons for health?

The first lesson is mergers are not a policy for tomorrow based on today's circumstances. Second, they are neither a euphemism for service reconfiguration, cutting manning levels and upping productivity, nor are they the political fig leaf of respectability, to disguise the need for closures and rationalisation. Third, mergers are a dangerous pastime that have demolished more organisations than they have built.

Private sector mergers are most inspired by the need to keep up with the share price expectations of stockholders. In the NHS that means mergers must demonstrate the dividend for the taxpayer will be in better services. Quite why an outraged public have not taken to the streets, demanding clapped out hospitals that gobble up their taxes don't go the same way as the turkey at Christmas, is beyond me.

Less than 10% of the NHS estate ever sees a patient. Try telling a shareholder in a retail chain that less than 40% of his estate is devoted to the core business of retailing.

Bill Gates, founder of the Microsoft Corporation, says: 'Size works against excellence.' All the evidence says he is right. The message seems to be to consider anything before you consider merging, including:

- breaking out niche markets
- downsizing
- process re-engineering
- lean production
- job design
- collaborative working
- partnerships
- franchising
- productive alliances
- performance management
- strategic coalitions
- value-adding partnerships.

Above all, remember, when Christmas is coming stay slim!

Change of thinking

The article caused a flutter of interest and there were the usual critics and those in agreement. The editor Dan Jellineck was pleased. Editors love controversy. Roy Lilley found himself being invited to speak on the subject of mergers to NHS audiences. As time went by, thinking became clearer – mergers were likely to be a bad thing for the NHS. Lilley said so and found himself at odds with ministers and the grey suits of Whitehall.

Little did anyone realise that within two-and-a-half years the Homewood NHS Trust in Surrey, where Roy Lilley was chairman and Eve Richardson chief executive, would be merged into oblivion.

The really important passage from the 'Two Turkeys' article turned out to be:

- The first lesson is that mergers are not a policy for tomorrow based on today's circumstances.

- Second, they are neither a euphemism for service reconfiguration, cutting manning levels and upping productivity, nor are they the political fig leaf of respectability, to disguise the need for closures and rationalisation.

- Third, mergers are a dangerous pastime that have demolished more organisations than they have built.

Any Trust manager, chief executive officer (CEO), board member or chairperson might like to rip this page out and stick it, with one of those funny magnet things, to the front door of the fridge, or even pin it up on the noticeboard in the office.

The message is: try everything before you resort to merging. Why? Because of the first sentence of the Turkey article: 'The first lesson is mergers are not a policy for tomorrow based on today's circumstances.'

Mergers are thought of as a convenient way to save cash. The evidence is the amount of cash saved is trifling compared to the grief and upset mergers cause. Nevertheless, mergers are once again on the political agenda in Whitehall, and that means they are on the lips of NHS managers up and down the country. The reasons to merge are no more legitimate this time around than they were the last time. There is only one reason to merge a service and that is to provide superior services. There is only one reason to cut the running costs of a Trust and that is because they are too high. One has nothing to do with the other.

Without realistic funding in health care, and real attack on the causes of ill-health (a subject that has nothing to do with the NHS), then the service will continue to dodge between the last crisis and the next. Duplication of services, lack of investment, poor managerial and clinical practice and downright selfishness, soak up the money that should be used for patient care.

The future points us in one direction, and the NHS points itself in another.

The real future is well beyond merging. The real future is understanding what is happening outside, in the real world beyond the Health Service, and employing the commonsense tactics of modern management. And that rarely includes merging.

Here is the real future – or perhaps not. As we can't be sure we must be prepared. Discussion points about the future of health care should be expressed in the language of business. Ideas will emerge that for many will be uncomfortable, for some preposterous, and for others familiar. Where health goes depends on radicalism. The NHS was born of radicalism and will only survive through managers and others who have the courage to be radical again.

Here are some radical ideas to help start your thinking processes and stimulate discussion. Copy them, circulate them, use them as ideas for brainstorming. Think of them as a pathway to tomorrow. Test them and tear them apart. But, and this is the most important part of the message:

Look at everything before you resort to mergers.

2
The Way Forward

Business processes will go and re-emerge as continuums

The NHS is process oriented. Some would say not processed enough. The fundamental of quality is about understanding what you have to do to get things right, first time, all the time and then repeating the process. Unfortunately, process in the NHS often reinforces bad practice and the 'getting it wrong' is duplicated, ingrained and part of the process. 'We've always done it that way.'

The NHS tries hard to focus on the needs of its 'customer', the patient. It generally fails because in most instances that involves the patient fitting in with the hospital's way of doing things. The NHS has not learned the lesson of the high street retailer, the all-night grocery store or 24-hour service.

How often do we hear the story of a patient taken into hospital on a Friday evening and kept in, until Monday morning, waiting for tests to be undertaken. When the hospital wakes up from its weekend nap and gets pathology and all the other testing and imaging services back to life, so the precious resource – the capital base of the NHS and the fixed overhead – is brought back to life. Drive past any hospital at the weekend or in the evening and the car park marked 'Doctors Only' (there are still such horrors) will be empty. The NHS is not a 24-hour, 365–days-a-year business. It has neither the money nor the will to achieve such a status. In consequence, resources and equipment lie as idle as the patients in their beds.

The patient is made to wait – that's the way it's done. There *are* alternatives. We can borrow from the real world of the service industry: continuum services. In the NHS continuum care would address these issues and would design the care of patients around the needs of patients. What patient in pain would object to having a hip replacement operation at 3am on a Bank Holiday Monday? The patient is used to all-night shopping and the 24-hour lifestyle that modern customers demand and take for granted.

The impact of 24-hour function on the NHS would be to bust the revenue account and drive staff to apoplexy. Policemen, firemen, ambulance services and airlines work around the clock. So why not the NHS? If there is not enough revenue in the system to fund 24-hour activity, then one assumption might be to close hospitals until there is. One hospital might do the work of three, organised properly and with the dead money taken out of the system. Closure, not merger. Tough to sell to politicians and a sceptical public.

The archetypal hip operation, so much used as the currency of discussion and parable in NHS circles, involves three main tranches of care: the support care before the operation to replace the painful joint; the operation and in-patient care itself, and then the service that supports the patient in the community, as they take their first careful steps back into normal function.

Hip operations are not cheap, but they are not expensive either. Ranging from £1,100 to £3,500 for a standard replacement for an elderly patient, you can bet the tranches of care either side of the in-patient episode, the 'either-side care', will be more expensive. Community physio, meals on wheels, adaptations to the home, dial-a-ride transport, day centre care, social bathing, community chiropody, health visiting, district nurse intervention, shopping services, domestic help, home alarm systems – the list is endless. Nevertheless, we still fund the segments of care from different budgets and from different organisations. Modern care will be continuum care. The interfaces between the organisations who provide the care will go, as they blend into one seamless service under one management strand. The fact that services for one episode of care, for one person, can be provided by such a range of different people, creates management interfaces that have to be managed, that duplicate effort and are costly. Less management less cost.

Discussion point: How would continuum care change funding mechanisms and what impact would it have on where you work and what you offer? How 'do-able' is the idea; are there any strands of the thinking that may be achievable in the short-term? Does the concept of new Health Action Zones make this prospect tougher or easier?

The customer will be the boss

Industry leaders used to say 'the customer is king', now they say the customer is king, president and God all rolled into one. The customerisation of health care is not far away. Patients are becoming better informed, they know more about what to expect, how to complain, and when to challenge. This is not comfortable for health care providers, but it is contributing to the zero-defect environment that is the expectation of the customer in today's demanding world. The impact on how health care works will be almost impossible to overstate. The savings that 'getting it right first time' might have to offer have never been estimated.

Discussion point: Is the 'customerisation' of the patient a good thing or a bad thing? What is the likely reaction of the medical profession? How will it impact on what you do?

Constant reorganisation

The most irritating words in the management dictionary are 'the management of change'. It is a ludicrous concept. A concept that supposes change is somehow strange or unexpected or different. Change is what management is all about. Without change, organisations need administrators and they are cheaper than managers.

Managers exist to manage change. Change is the day-to-day, the routine and the normal. As technology moves us into undreamed-of possibilities, so too health care will change. It will change from where it is delivered, from who delivers it and how it is delivered. That is the change agenda that wraps services around the needs of the patient, in a place convenient to the patient, at a time that is convenient to the patient and by whomsoever the patient has the most faith in. Technology will drive change. Faster and faster in a spiral – a vortex. Managers will learn that today's solutions will not endure much beyond tomorrow.

Structures cannot be set in concrete. Strategies become a ludicrous concept. In a world where airlines sell pensions, petrol stations sell bread and grocers are bankers – who will be bold enough or stupid enough to try and predict the future in a five-year strategic plan? All the modern manager has are tactics and techniques. The techniques to deal with the day-to-day and tactics to deal with the unexpected. A new language, new definitions of management, decoupled from the rigidity of strategy and management chained to a redundant past.

Discussion point: In industry, particularly the service industries, it is common for brands to be relaunched and services re-invented to keep pace with customer expectation. How practical is that for health care? Are you flexible enough to be in a constant state of change? Are you sufficiently in touch with patient demand to know what they want – can you fund their expectations? Or is it not about money? Will a National Institute for Clinical Excellence make any difference 'on the ground'?

Co-payments

As politicians do the rounds touting promises that cannot be squared – better services for less taxes – the NHS and its managers and clinicians pay the price of performing increasingly cost-effectively. Uncomfortable changes might be in sight. Co-payments means that patients who are able to, make a contribution to the cost of their health care. This is a common feature of European systems.

In the UK, wheelchair users can have a standard NHS chair or a voucher – so they can add to the value of the voucher, with their own money, to get something better. As drug therapies become more expensive how long will it be before families demand the right to top up the money the NHS has available to spend, to secure the latest drug or therapy, too expensive for commissioners to provide as part of a core service?

The debate is: do we have the right, by our own wealth or will, to create a multi-tiered health service that fits our pockets and our consciences?

Discussion point: How comfortable are you with the idea of taking money from patients for treatment? Would you avoid the option? Do you think patients should have the option to pay if they want to? How would you cope with a pay and non-pay service?

IT will be everything

It used to be said that money made the world go around. Not any more. It is the management of information by the use of technology that makes the money go around. Health care, poorly served by IT in the past, must wake up to the possibilities.

The Internet, now moved out of the anorak age and hobby status, is playing a serious part in leisure and business activity. It is set to inform patients in a way that they have never been before. Special interest groups, forums, information – it is all on the Internet. Information for doctors is read by patients and patients can let their views be known to challenge the medical profession.

Hospital performance data can be routinely posted on the Internet for the world to witness.

Pharmaceutical suppliers are struggling to comply with legislation shaped in the days of the printed word – against the demand from the public to know more about the effects and side effects of the drugs they are prescribed. Self-administered AIDS tests are illegal in the UK but freely and legally available for import, from suppliers connectable through the Internet. Patients will drive the agenda.

The NHS will discover the savings to be had from IT, and learn it is not necessary to invent and own every part of the system. Enabling things to happen is as important a role as doing it. The US military sub-contracts its Internet requirements to a French IT supplier, and uses the public US network for transmission. The army pay-to-play. They own nothing, they just use what they want and pay for it. Encryption takes care of the most sensitive material. A computer the size of Moscow would take a lifetime to unscramble even routine messages.

The NHS and its fears about secrecy, confidentiality and encryption will catch up and cash in on the savings to be had from: medical records kept on smart card; digital imaging; tele-medicine; delivery-by-post pharmacy, and ward-ordering systems. What the world takes for granted, the NHS is waking up to, and the rewards in cost savings will be stunning.

Discussion point: Is the NHS too far behind in the implementation of IT to catch up? Does the NHS over-complicate IT? Is a 'pay to play' option credible for the NHS? Why does the NHS get IT so spectacularly wrong? Where IT has 'worked' – why?

Public services are just concepts

Enabling services to 'happen' is a trick that local government was slow to learn. Indeed, it was legislation that provided the catalyst for action. Local government now takes out-sourcing and enabling for granted, and the savings in cost and improvements in services have been colossal.

The Department of Health tried to kick-start the market testing agenda but messed up badly with the timing. Their paper 'Competing for Quality', encouraging hospitals to look at out-sourcing and market testing as a way to ease costs and make quality more reliable, was published at the time when Trusts were in the early days of establishing themselves. Trusts had too much in the 'in-tray' to be bothered with anything but getting to grips with operational problems. Subsequent attempts to force the pace of market testing and outsourcing have failed to deliver the returns that were to benefit local government. There is still much to be done and huge savings to be had in running costs.

There has been no such impetus in the NHS, and Trusts, with congested priorities taking them elsewhere, have been slow to realise the potential for outsourcing and service providers under contract.

Let's look at two 'holy-grail' departments in most Trusts, human resource and finance departments.

Human resource departments have to demonstrate their worth in an environment where engaging staff on local terms has become taboo, and where managers are quite capable of hiring, firing, training, disciplining and managing their staff. Every pound spent on health care has to show it is a pound invested, giving a pound's worth of return. Human resource communities will find it increasingly difficult to justify their existence.

As the internal market gives way to a financial environment without the rigours of the private sector and the encumbrance of each transaction being accounted for, so the finance departments will wither on the vine. Following the Local Authority example, how long will it be before a bright finance director organises a management buy-out of his department, computerises the systems, and offers an agency service to 20 or 30 Trusts – whose needs are all basically the same. That saves real money, year in, year out.

Discussion point: How happy are you with out-sourcing more of what you do? Would you feel out of control, or in more control? Would you extend out-sourcing to medical services? Perhaps to pharmaceutical companies? Does it matter 'who does what' as long as it is good?

Lottery cash will fund R&D

The lid has been taken off the box. Lottery cash is already earmarked to fund healthy living centres. How long will the politicians resist cost pressures in the NHS, and allow R&D (research and development) to be funded by the profits of our national flutter? And why not, might say a public that supports good causes and sees the NHS as no better a cause than any other?

In some countries health services are supported by lottery contributions. Opera lovers might have a hard time explaining why their aspirations take precedence over the needs of an NHS left to sing for its supper. This is a difficult debate and government will need to give a lead. In an environment where the words 'the people' are appearing more frequently in both policy and political speeches, the 'people's lottery' may well find much of its proceeds spent on the 'people's health'.

Discussion point: How do you feel about your Lottery flutter finding its way into the NHS? Is this a better way to fund public services? Should the idea be extended? What happens when folk switch their spending to other things?

What future does primary care have?

A primary-care-led NHS was nothing more than a carefully chosen phrase in a politician's speech. It was designed to mean nothing. The phrase, without boundaries, has come to mean everything. It has come to conjure images of enthusiastic GPs performing everything but the kitchen sink, in the kitchen sink, or on the kitchen table. More sensibly, primary care is convenient, parochial and sensible. Local, convenient, and increasingly familiar.

Everyone likes the idea, except Acute hospitals, who have their future visions obscured by a lack of clarity and the loss of cash that 'primary-care-led' means – and the Treasury. As the Treasury watch GPs spend fortunes constructing care facilities, and as outcomes do not appear to improve, and as costs rise and risks go up, eventually someone will say: 'Let's save some money, get some supervision into the system, and put this lot into one place and call it a hospital'. Vertically integrated care as in Detroit, USA, is a great model to solve the health care problems of the inner city. Patients arrive at accident and emergency departments for all their needs. The statistics would seem to show that patients are voting with their feet and that it is starting to happen here. A&E (accident and emergency) admissions are on the increase. The reasons are complex and the total picture obscure. But the factors in the equation say patients will go where they can get seen fast and reliably. In some inner city areas, where primary care is poor and uninviting for GPs to set up shop, a first port of call to an A&E department with its facilities open all hours is an attractive proposition.

Discussion point: Vertically integrated care, as it is called in the USA, is a good way to provide primary and secondary care together, where inner-city conditions mitigate against the conventional approach. Is primary care really a 'gate-keeper'? Would vertically integrated care save, or cost money?

What's next?

Looking into the crystal ball, divining the future, is a mug's game. By the time you know if you are right, it's too late! One thing is certain. The world is travelling in the direction of downsizing, returning to core business, growing bigger by getting smaller. It is not merging, it is taking things over, being ruthless about waste and poor practice, subsuming and making alliances. It is not hoping to cut its costs by getting together; it is hoping to improve its services to customers – by getting together. The NHS's direction of travel is in the opposite direction. Getting bigger, costing more, moving away from the customer, confused and directionless. The word merger is on no one's lips but the NHS's and that speaks volumes.

Before you speak the word, speak some other words and run these thoughts by the team you are working with:

- breaking out niche markets
- process re-engineering
- lean production
- job design
- collaborative working
- partnerships

- franchising
- productive alliances
- performance management
- strategic coalitions
- value-adding partnerships.

They come from the language of business. They are the techniques of modern management, they work, they change organisations, and they deliver. Think about what they might mean as an alternative strategy to merger. The gain might be the same, but the pain might be very different.

The final question you must answer, using a pop-music idiom, is to tell me what you want, what you really, really want. If the answer is a merger, be sure you know what you're getting into. Be prepared, good luck and read on!

3

The Homewood NHS Trust: a personal perspective

Eve Richardson (former Chief Executive)

I welcomed the opportunity for Homewood to become a first-wave NHS Trust, not to defend its status and territory, but because it helped us in a planned and evolving change process which had started in 1983.

Homewood provided services to people with learning disabilities; to those with mental health needs; and to older people who were also mentally frail. Around two-thirds of its core activity was in the provision of services for people with learning disabilities. The primary objective was moving people out of institutional settings into new environments in their local communities.

We also offered major expertise in supporting people with severe and challenging behaviour. Alongside delivering this major change programme, we were working with our purchasers to develop local services for people with mental health needs, as well as services for older people who were physically and mentally frail.

Our major challenge was the complication of working in partnership with 34 purchasers, to prepare people with learning disabilities to move to new and appropriate homes. Within our local communities we also wanted to develop a range of support networks. In all areas the key was in establishing partnerships, and aiming to provide integrated care packages for individuals in new and flexible ways.

Following the NHS reforms of 1990, as a Trust, and in pursuit of our long-term objectives, we developed a close working relationship with the second-wave Weybourne Community Trust, as well as with: GPs and fundholders; a variety of social services departments, particularly with our three local directors; with housing departments and associations; with the Education Service; and a variety of voluntary and private organisations.

My role as chief executive was not only to provide internal leadership, but to reach out and develop all the key external relationships. When I arrived, I inherited over a thousand people with learning disabilities living in over-crowded and institutional environments on our main campus. By the time of our merger with Weybourne, the resettlement programme was virtually completed.

A creative joint venture around the future use of the unused part of the Homewood estate had been completed, which promised a large capital investment for the new organisation.

We were a radical Trust, but we had always been radical, perhaps too much so for our day. I remember, long before the publications 'Working for Patients' and 'Caring for People', working closely with our local Health and Social Services colleagues on the option to set up a new Health and Social Care Agency. Regrettably, this was not a vehicle open to us all to pursue under the reforms and it became increasingly difficult to work together – eligibility criteria, contracts and competition got in the way.

Clearly I remember, in 1989, at our initial presentation of our Trust application to Region, taking along a truly multi-agency, as well multi-disciplinary team which included a psychiatrist, a Social Service director, a Housing Association director, and the general manager of the unit that was to become the Weybourne Trust. Instead of being pleased with the range of local support, the comment was *'why have you brought along your potential competitors?'*. Clearly, we were too far ahead of our time. Integrated care? Why should this not be important for these client groups as well as everyone else!

Throughout our time as Homewood it was essential for me to look ahead to our longer-term direction. This grew increasingly important as we successfully resettled a large proportion of the people in our service to 33 other local communities. We had looked seriously at a franchising model, but we decided that we did not believe that it was right for people with learning disabilities. They needed genuine community presence and integration, not more artificial boundaries and agencies.

We continued to work closely with Weybourne. They provided generic primary care to our service users in the community. As community-based chief executives, Weybourne's CEO and I joined a Kings Fund learning set together, exploring future options.

As our services were so closely entwined, we had considered the option of merging our services under one Trust application. But it was judged to be too soon. Both organisations had complex change agendas with new models of care to be introduced. To have focused on merger then would have de tracted from our respective priorities of reconfiguring care. The informal agreement was that if we were successful in delivering our major agendas, we would revisit merger again within five years.

In 1993 we were both well down the road of successfully delivering our agendas and were both looking at the future. Our preference was a still more radical agency, with Social Services and Housing joining us. However, the time was not right and the rules and climate would not allow it. So late in 1993 discussions started at board level about the benefits of merger. It was considered a natural progression and next step; not looked at through rose-coloured glasses.

While both Trusts shared the same future vision and values around care, we knew that we had very different styles and cultures. Homewood's pioneering streak was in contrast to Weybourne's more cautious approach to change. However, it was felt that there could be benefit for the future in combining these styles. After all it would be a new organisation and not a replica of the old. Well, that was the theory!

During 1994 we set up a joint merger project team and quickly established joint processes. To create certainty and avoid a management vacuum, we included the appointment of acting executive directors. It is always most difficult at board level when you have two of everyone!

I created one less problem by deciding that it was time for me to move on to a new career. I felt that over ten years I had achieved my objectives for the organisation. I had seen it through four reorganisations already!

Rightly or wrongly, Roy Lilley, my chairman, also decided it was time to move on. He felt we had come to the end of an era at Homewood. So it meant that some tough decisions had been made. Telling this to our team and to our staff was more difficult, as they were very proud of what we had achieved. We tried to do this sensitively and we took our time. I stayed in post until shadow board stage and then took a well-earned sabbatical. I felt that with the appointment of all my executive directors to the shadow board the key strands of our legacy were safe in their hands.

What are my thoughts nearly three years on? I believe that the merger process was carried out well, because we consulted, listened, gained support and won hearts and minds. I have not returned to the new organisation because I genuinely believe in moving on. So it is not me who can judge whether our vision of a new culture while taking the best of both has been achieved.

I do know that all my old team, the executive directors we left in place, have now moved on. Even though all of them have achieved promotions, it leaves a nagging doubt. Was a new organisation really developed? Perhaps, to many staff, Homewood and Weybourne coming together as Bournewood may have felt like a bigger Weybourne. Perhaps developing a totally new culture with key leaders from the past is just not achievable. Is it desirable or even practical, within the NHS, to start with a clean slate and develop a new culture? It takes a great deal of time.

Was it all worthwhile? The acid test for me will be around the benefits to service users. Has the planned integration of services and flexible delivery been achieved? If not, then we will need to think more creatively about the future options, because mergers without service benefits are expensive in terms of time, money and people – and achieve almost nothing.

4

The Homewood NHS Trust: a personal perspective

Roy Lilley (former Chairman)

The honour of chairing the first-wave Trust, Homewood, in Chertsey, Surrey, was the most enjoyable, entertaining, difficult, frustrating and challenging thing I have ever done. Leaving it was the most painful moment of my business life.

Good fortune and good luck had left me in a position to indulge my interest for public services. I had the time and few other distractions. I could give Homewood my whole attention.

As a service, born of the days when good-hearted folk thought the best way to deal with learning-disabled people and mental health sufferers was to create a community for them, and tuck them away from public gaze – it was horrible.

Botleys Park was the parkland in which a village had been built. A medieval fiefdom. Self-sufficient, self-effacing, and self-exiled. Mad or bad, the laws of the day did not discriminate. The Northwest Surrey Learning Disability and Mental Health Unit lived in the shadow of a water-tower, and had the feel of a prison and the despair of a community of castaways. An institution isolated in the acres of Botleys Park.

The staff battled with a crumbling estate, inappropriately placed residents and clients, and the whole place lived on love. There was never enough money and no chance of getting any more – competing with the glamour services of the Acute sector, bouncing bonny babies, and dancing grannies with new hips. How could difficult and disturbed behaviour ever compete?

Trust status allowed us to make some changes, but it was clear from the start that institutional care was entirely wrong for the majority of those who lived their lives at Botleys or who were treated there. Homewood, which took its name from the woodlands surrounding the site, needed to be a community-based service.

Homewood became the first NHS Trust to achieve BS 5750 (ISO9000) as a quality mark for the whole of its services. It won the coveted Investors in People award; and became the only Trust to achieve a 'no-strike' deal with its staff. Important and ground-breaking – but still, first and foremost, an institution.

Good working relations made better by the close personal relationships between the senior managers meant that to merge services with the neighbouring Weybourne Community NHS Trust was an obvious choice. Informal soundings between the chairs and chief executives lead to cautious discussion at board level, and the formal announcement that a merger might transform Homewood services to having a foundation in the community.

The convolutions of the processes and the time it took have blurred into the past. I do recall they were hall-marked with affability and mutual respect. Homewood had the good fortune to turn a large part of its redundant site into offices and a parkland for the community. I shall always be grateful to the members and officers of Runnymead Borough Council, who shared our vision of the future and did everything they could to turn Homewood's wasteland into a multi-million pound dowry for the successor organisation.

Homewood and Weybourne became Bournewood, and not Weywood as I had mischievously hoped it would be named. By and large there were few job casualties, although most of the Homewood senior management team have gone on to do other things in bigger organisations or to more important jobs.

Bournewood decided not to extend the benefits of BS 5750 to the whole of its services, and the Investor in People Accreditation was withdrawn. Approaching 70 per cent of Homewood staff enjoyed the benefits of locally negotiated pay and conditions. Under Bournewood that has withered, and there was no attempt to extend it.

I now have no contact with Bournewood; I decided early in the merger discussions that Homewood would be my last public appointment, and chose to stand down at the end of my contract. Every day I think about the residents, patients, clients, staff and volunteers who made my time with them so happy.

Homewood was leading-edge, some said reckless, I say willing to give everything a try – if it could be shown there was a benefit for the people we served. I feel a strong sense of disappointment at the way in which so much of what Homewood pioneered has evaporated. Gone, I suppose, because times have changed and priorities moved on.

I have never been back to Bournewood. For five years Homewood was for me a way of life, a way of life that has changed for me and them. A life that I battled to de-institutionalise, that in turn left its mark by institutionalising me!

Homewood is an example of mergers working and working well for the right reasons. I think we saved the cost of duplication at board level and some operational small change. The real gain was in the way in which the services were delivered, and that mattered – nothing else does.

What have I learned? Communication is the key. Good news or bad, be straight with people. Take people into your confidence, they will seldom let you down. If they know what's going on they don't have to make anything up. You can kill the gossip.

Get out from behind your desk and go and talk to people. They can't be on your side unless you invite them; they can't help you unless you tell them what you want. Have a clear vision, share it with them and work for it together; get the best people around you and go for it.

Mergers are difficult, don't underestimate how difficult, and only in the rarest circumstances are they a solution to the problems of modern health care. They are mostly a fig leaf to cover up for weak management unable to face tough decisions. If you put off the evil day, the evil day will come and find you.

My merger was a good one for the right reasons, but is still personally painful, and I think, painful too for the executives and non-executives who played their part so magnificently.

The camaraderie, the sense of team belonging and mutual achievement were very strong. That is something I confess I have never been able to duplicate, never experienced in my business life, and am unlikely ever to recapture again.

My time at Homewood was magic and the merger a miracle – good luck with yours!

Part 2

101 Questions about Mergers and Change for Managers, Board Members and the Truly Determined!

You bought a book expecting 101 questions but here is a bonus, this is number 102!

It is the first question – it is also the $64,000 question, the hot question, the toughest question and the last question. Answer this one first and then go to Question 1. Work your way to Question 101 and then come back to this one, again! Keep trying to answer this question and make this question the rider to every other question. Make it *the stripe in the toothpaste* question running through your whole thought processes...

Is merger inevitable – what are the alternatives?

Mergers of organisations are complex, time consuming and fraught with difficulties. Very few people have experience of doing it and the ones that have seldom want to go through the experience again. Indeed, mergers are very 'personal' things and the successful ones are about understanding the sensitivities that exist and how to get the best out of organisations by coaxing them together, rather than crashing them into each other. Mergers cannot solve the problems of poor management, neither are they a substitute for proper funding. Is merging the only way, what are the alternatives, and could they produce a better outcome?

- Is the merger covering up for poor management – is a shake-out of incompetent people a tougher but better alternative?

- Is joint or closer working with neighbouring services all that is required?

- Would an independent and realistic assessment of current services, highlighting poor ones, be enough to discontinue some services in favour of the ones you are good at?

- Can costs be contained by pooling some 'back office' services, such as merging finance departments or joint-venturing pathology services?

- Can you strengthen the organisation by 'acquiring' a neighbouring organisation in a voluntary takeover rather than a merger?

1. Does everyone understand why the merger is taking place?

In later questions we explore the reasons why a merger may happen (or not). However, early in the process there has to be an understanding of the imperatives for change. Whatever they may be and how they might emerge, it is important that the real reasons are understood by those who will be leading the process. Leadership is vital to the success of a merger and a leader cannot 'lead' if there is no understanding of the real motives.

- Who has real ownership of the concept?

- Who is in the driving seat, who has the power?

- Will the 'owner' be prepared to be recognised? Will Region say 'Yes, we want you to merge to save money', or will they keep silent?

- Do individual or career motivations play a part in the decisions?

- Will you be in a position to be honest with people about what the real reasons are?

2. Is the merger service driven?

Why is the merger taking place? In the world outside health care, mergers take place to gain access to new markets, cut costs or provide for research and development. In the NHS the reasons can be very similar. Understanding why a merger or change is taking place and what the drivers are will play an important part in its acceptance. Service driven mergers can be brought about to improve services, develop service or reduce services. Which is it?

- Has there been a thorough review of services?

- Who has conducted it?

- Was it independent?

- Does everyone accept the results?

- Does it matter if they don't?

- How are the commissioners involved?

- What is the role of the medical directors in service reviews?

- Are the staff consulted?

- Are the public consulted?

- What is the role of the CHC (Community Health Council)?

- Does a service review point to a full merger or can some services be left to one provider, or other solutions?

- Is geography an issue?

- What are the financial implications?

- What are the implications for staff?

3. Is the merger financially driven?

Of all the reasons for merger this can be the most internally painful. Finance driven can only mean reducing costs and that almost always has an impact on staff, careers and families. In addition, cutting costs is not always a reason to bring two organisations together. There are often other ways to cut costs. The evidence is that two organisations with financial problems do not, necessarily, produce an organisation that is finance 'problem-free'. Alternatively, a financially driven merger might be the product of an investment strategy, aimed at producing a solid and well founded base to address future needs.

- Are the financial assumptions and projections correct?

- What are the real underlying issues?

- How have they been arrived at?

- Who carried out the work?

- Are they independent?

- How were they chosen?

- Do they have the necessary specialism to understand the nuances of what they are being asked to undertake?

- Is merger the only solution?

- Can out-sourcing, delayering, re-evaluation of services, produce the desired result?

- In the long term, will the new organisation be any better off?

- What are the future investment opportunities?

- Is there an overarching investment strategy for the Region?

- What is the impact of weighted capitation shifts?

- If the merger is financially viable today, what will, or could, change to destabilise it in the future?

- Do you know the answer?

- Does anybody?

4. Is the merger politically driven?

In an environment where politicians of all main political parties recoil at the thought of putting up taxes, set against a background of increased demand, reducing costs through mergers is an attractive proposition. A merger may not be a local imperative, but regionally there may be no other answer. This is the most difficult merger of all to manage. The Regional Office is staffed by civil servants who are the instruments of delivering government policies. If you are caught up in merger proposals that are clearly politically driven and do not appear to deliver realistic benefits for patients, then boards, managers and others need to think carefully how they express their concerns and what they do in the public arena to oppose such a merger.

- What is the possibility of the board influencing the politics?
- How do managers react?
- Is there likely to be campaigning from outside the organisation or among staff?
- Who will handle it?
- Can the board influence outside organisations to influence the political outcome?
- Should they?
- What can be done to establish the views of local and national politicians?
- Do the members of the board, or the chair, have regular meetings with politicians?
- Are politicians welcomed into the organisation?
- Do politicians 'pop-in' – or wait for an invitation?
- Do trade unions and local employer organisations have views, and will they express them?
- Local support, user and pressure groups will have views; who will collate them?
- How influential is the CHC?

5. Is the merger Region driven?

Merger timetables are the purview of Regions. Regions have to deliver a political agenda, in many instances favouring merger and at the same time ensuring comprehensive cover meeting patients' needs. Regional offices are expected to prepare reports for ministers about service configurations and submissions must assess the initial proposals against the next best options and against the status quo, in a full option appraisal.

- How can you influence regional reports to ministers?

- How will you ensure the quality of your own optional appraisal?

- How can you be sure your own appraisal will form the basis of the Region's report to ministers?

- Formal consultation is in the responsibility of Region – how can you influence the process?

- The CHC have to be formally consulted – how will you influence them?

- Alternative options include disestablishment or an acquisition – have you assessed the options against the Region's criteria?

- Do you understand the requirements of the NHS and Community Care Act 1990, in respect of merger?

- Have the board got copies of the relevant parts of the Act?

6. Is this a merger or a takeover?

A merger is seldom the coming together of two equal partners. Is this really a merge, or is a weaker partner being subsumed into a stronger organisation?

- Which part of the partnership are you?
- Are you being really frank about your strengths and weaknesses?
- Have you got the best partner?
- Is there anyone else to partner, or work with?
- Are you being forced into an unwelcome 'marriage'?
- Are you seeking someone else's assets; are your assets the prize?
- Would better use of your assets avoid the pain of a merger?
- Will your 'part' of the merge disappear, or will some of your identity remain?
- Is this a marriage made in heaven – or hell?

7. Are there good reasons to resist a merger?

A merger may not be the best answer to your problems. This may not mean *every* merger, it might mean *this* merger. Agreeing to merge is about the organisation understanding itself and its future.

- A merger may just be following a trend – is the trend sustainable?

- If a merger is about improving performance, will some tougher management or a change in style at the top produce the answer?

- Where there is no support at all for a merger, will persisting cause irrevocable damage?

- Have you explored all other management opportunities to avoid a merger?

8. Will the merger benefit patients or the treasury?

Service driven mergers are widely thought to be the soundest reason for organisations to get together. Better services for patients is always a comfortable sounding reason! If the reason is financial – there is just not enough money to go around – expect a lot more opposition. Do not muddle the two reasons or pretend the aim is better services when the commissioner is going quietly broke! Be honest.

• Can the real benefits for patients be quantified?

• Will they be clearly recognisable to the community?

• Will the clinicians endorse the patient benefit argument?

• How will GPs react?

• If the real reason is lack of finance, can savings be translated into longer-term patient benefits and service improvements?

• If financially driven mergers produce a greater critical mass, can improvements (such as reduction in junior doctors' hours), be expressed as a tangible benefit?

9. Can you establish all of the benefits a merger might deliver?

Some of the benefits of merger may not be obvious. A detailed analysis of the total impact of a merger may reveal improvements in working practice, or savings in duplication, that may tip the balance in the perception of staff or the public that may help a merger proceed much more smoothly. Can you find 'something for everyone'?

- Who is best placed to carry out a SWOT (strengths, weaknesses, opportunities and threats) analysis of the benefits?

- Should the work be carried out in-house or would an independent analysis carry more weight?

- Can you demonstrate long-term benefits that may outweigh any short-term disruption?

- What merger alternatives are included in a SWOT analysis?

- Can you identify the resources required to carry out this work?

10. What can you do to learn from other organisations who have gone through merger experiences?

Although each merger is different and no two organisations are the same, some lessons are transferable. Talking to others who have been through the process, or perhaps decided not to merge, will be a worthwhile exercise.

* Can you identify organisations who may have lessons to pass on?

* Who should make the approach?

* Should different parts of the organisation be encouraged to talk to their counterparts?

* Do you know the questions you need answers to?

* Can you rely on others being frank with you?

* Can you compare notes with more than one organisation?

* Are you able to talk to people who have been displaced by merger – how were they treated and what can you learn about how you should handle your 'people' issues?

11. Can you recognise merger pitfalls?

An enthusiasm for merger is not a good enough reason to merge. Indeed the enthusiasms may obscure the sense of reality that is needed to make the project succeed. Knowing what the pitfalls are and where they may appear is an essential ingredient for success.

- Is *merger mania* producing distorted expectations?

- How will you avoid the merger becoming an end in itself – instead of a continuing part of the management agenda?

- Will premature actions send the wrong message?

- How do you plan to bring the merger into the open?

- Are you willing to recognise mistakes and admit to them?

- How open will the process be?

- Will you try to pretend the only news about the merger is good news – or are you prepared to be realistic?

- Mergers need to be managed for longer than you think – when will you be able to stop managing yours?

12. Should the merger be assessed against winners and losers criteria?

Only a fool thinks a merger is universally good news. There are always winners and losers. The winners will annoy the losers and the losers might work at undermining the success of the end result. Knowing who is in the winning category and who is in the losing category is key.

- How will you identify the winners?
- Why are they winners?
- How will you identify the losers?
- Why are they losers?
- Can you change them into winners?
- What will it take?
- Is it worth it?

13. How does the merger feel?

Does the organisation have a 'feel-good' factor? Are you able to recognise it? There may also be a 'feel-bad' factor. An organisation is made up of people and all of those people have feelings. Often these feelings can transpose themselves into a corporate 'feeling'. Difficult to explain and harder to identify, getting out and about in the organisation, talking to the people who work there, gives an interesting insight into how the organisation feels about its future. The merger process is not just about the board, the project team or key managers. It is about everyone, with any responsibility, tuning into the organisation and listening very carefully to the messages that are sent back.

- How much time do you earmark for walking around the organisation talking to people?
- Is there a night shift – when did you last pay a visit?
- Does the organisation work at weekends – when did you last visit?
- Is there a schedule for out-of-hours visiting?
- Do you feel comfortable just 'popping-in'?
- Are you able to sense the mood of the organisation?
- Do you make a point of talking to people who are opposed to your ideas?
- Do you think people tell you what you want to hear?
- What do you do to avoid that?

14. If a merger seems a good idea now, what will it be like in five years?

Is the merger a solution to short-term problems? Have you tried every possible alternative to merger, including some of the tougher ones of downsizing, management buy-outs and out-sourcing? A merger may bring a solution to a problem but can also bring just as many problems. Think about the future; what will have changed, what will the management landscape look like in five years' time? Can you map the future and predict the outcome of a merger against the likely political and economic changes ahead?

- Is the merger a short-term solution to a long-term problem?

- Is there a real need for your organisation to exist at all?

- In the longer term, is this merger simply a precursor to another merger later on?

- Does this merger include enough of the key players? Should there be more than one other partner? Perhaps two or three?

15. Is there a strong anti-merger faction?

Like it or not, the people who work in the organisation will have a view about an impending merger or major change. They will have views and will find ways of making them known. Some of the views may be passionately held and arrived at out of genuine feelings or a fear of the unknown. Management's job is to make a judgement on what is best for the organisation, the people it serves and the men and women who work there. A strong history, a pride in the organisation and genuine feelings of attachment can mitigate against a merger being popular. A strong anti-merger faction can occupy disproportionate management time and resources. While everything that can be done should be done, recognising the strength of the anti-merger lobby and developing a strategy to deal with it is an unavoidable consequence.

- How strong is the anti-merger/change sentiment?

- Is the senior team really aware of the strength of feeling?

- What measures are in place to ensure that the board understands the real feelings of the anti-faction?

- What is the reason for the strength of feeling?

- Does history play a part?

- Are there politics involved?

- What is the hidden agenda?

- Does it boil down to a fear of losing jobs?

- Is there a genuine attachment to much-needed services?

- Are the anti-mergers right?

16. If you make pre-merger promises, can you keep them?

If mergers are to provide solutions for organisations, then they will have to provide solutions for the individuals who are involved. Will the merger provide better services, better job opportunities and improvements for all? The temptation for managers – particularly middle managers who may be unemployed as a result of the merger – is to promise everyone everything. After all, delivering on promises is not their problem. Even undertakings given in good faith may be scrapped by an incoming management team.

- Who is authorised to give pre-merger undertakings?
- What is the documentation procedure?
- Does everyone (inside the organisation and outside) know what to expect from a post-merger organisation?
- Who will be held to account for undertakings?
- When negotiations get tricky, how will 'promising your way out of problems' be resisted?
- Are the people in a position to give undertakings going to be part of the emerging organisation?
- Can you secure undertakings with the incoming management?

17. Do you have the managerial capacity to handle a merger?

Merging an organisation is a time consuming and tricky business. Trying to accomplish a pain-free merger and at the same time carry on running the organisation is next to impossible. A merger programme is not a hobby to be done in the evenings and weekends. A successful merge will need the skills of the best people, not folk who can be operationally side-lined or who will be passed over when merger time comes. As the merger gets closer and the work piles up – something will suffer. If a merge is coming about because of the poor management of one of the merge partners, or because of resource problems – are both partners strong enough to see a merge through without something collapsing? Is this merge a takeover – what is the impact? There is an obligation to appoint a project manager. The leadership role of this appointment is vital. The project manager does not have to be one of the participating chief executives.

- Who is the project manager to be?
- How will they be chosen?
- Who is planning the resources needed to move into a merge?
- Is there a meetings schedule?
- How realistic is it and what is the allowance for contingency and slippage?
- What is the estimate of resources required – managerial, secretarial and backup?
- How is it to be funded?
- Are the merger team expected to hold down operational responsibilities at the same time?
- What are the service implications?
- Can the merger team be decoupled from day-to-day responsibility while the merger programme progresses?
- What is the likely impact on morale, and the knock-on effect on the quality of the organisation's performance?
- If talks collapse or resources just will not allow for the merge negotiations to be conducted sensibly – can the merge be turned into a takeover, or ended?
- What is the impact and likely hostility?
- Does it matter?

18. Does the top team have the skills?

Running a large and complex organisation is one thing; running a merger programme is another. The skills needed for one may not translate into the skills required to make a success of the other. The top team may not be the top team to survive the merge and may well have their own motives for how they work or behave. Negotiating skills are top of the list and the top team, used to managing, rather than negotiating, may have difficulty.

- What are the team skills required?

- What are the individual skills required?

- How will the top team's skills be assessed against the requirements to making a success of the merger?

- What are their training requirements?

- Is there time to give them the extra training they might need?

- Who is best placed to provide the training?

- How will 'personal agendas' impact on the success of the merger programme?

21. What arrangements do you have to make to set up a new legal entity?

A new Trust, the product of merged organisations, is a new entity in law and only comes into being when the component Trusts have been 'dissolved'. All of the provisions of the NHS and Community Care At 1990 apply – just like setting up a new Trust. Relevant sections of the NHS and Community Care Act 1990 set out the arrangements and criteria for a Trust dissolution, merger and re-establishment. It is important to fully understand these and to determine which type of reconfiguration arrangements apply to you both formally and informally.

- Have there been informal discussions between the Trust boards around the reconfiguration options and future legal arrangements?

- Have they led to clear, formal board agreements that are minuted about the proposed way forward?

- Have the accounting arrangements around a merger or an acquisition been followed?

- What legal advice will you take?

- Do you have an agreed joint action plan?

22. How will you know you are getting the best legal advice?

The reconfiguration of existing Trusts will require the careful drafting of three legal documents around dissolution, transfer orders and an establishment statutory instrument. It will be essential for boards to carefully consider these documents and to ensure that they receive sound legal advice. The temptation will be to assume that all Trusts are the same and a standard document would suffice. This is not the case as Trusts can be very different in the ownership of land and property, sometimes with the added complication of trust fund and charity interests.

- Who will draw up the legal specification?
- How will you select your solicitors?
- Should they be specialists?
- Will you use more than one firm in the total process?
- Will it be a joint process?
- Does the board understand that it is not possible to have one firm of solicitors acting for two Trusts?
- Who will decide?
- When will you set up this process?
- What briefing arrangements will you set up with the board?
- How will you know that you have value for money?
- What 'milestones' can be put in place to ensure that the process does not become protracted?
- How does the time schedule allow for contingency?
- How does the legal process fit into the overall scheme?

23. Do you understand the financial implications of your chosen route?

Under the NHS & Community Care Act 1990, Treasury consent is required for financial actions which follow dissolution and establishment. Write-off debt is a Treasury responsibility and the new originating capital debt requires Treasury's approval at every stage. The debt structure can affect the viability of the Trust and should be a key part of the planning and evaluation process. Creation of new Originating Capital Debt (OCD) are matters of government finance and open to Parliamentary challenge, and therefore require careful handling and presentation. The write-off of public debt is a sensitive subject. The Treasury needs to understand whether the write-off arises through devaluation of fixed assets or from poor financial performance, or a combination of these or other factors.

- Is there transparency around year-on-year changes between reconfigured or newly established Trusts?
- Have standard and accepted accounting practices been followed?
- Does the board understand the financial principles?
- Where did the advice come from?
- Is it independent and reliable?
- Does the board understand any new financial responsibilities?
- What is the role of the Treasury and Region, and does the board understand this?
- Does the board understand the requirements and submissions from these key players?
- What is the time-table process?
- Is Treasury agreement likely to delay the process?
- Is there contingency in the time-table?
- Has the Treasury verified the auditors?

24. Does the board understand the impact of transferring balances?

Assets transferring between NHS organisations must be valued on a consistent basis in accordance with NHS accounting policy, in the books of the old and new owners. The Trust manual for accounts instructs that transfer of assets between NHS organisations must be at net book value. The current book valuation of assets prepared by the District Valuer may be adequate for Trust merger purposes and no new valuation may be needed, but this is a complex area and Trusts must seek the advice of Region in respect of valuations and certifying assets and liabilities. There are also special rules that apply to reserves and for procedures for repaying public debt ahead of schedule. Arrangement for the write-off of short-or long-term loans must be the subject of discussion with Region.

- Is the board satisfied with the financial advice at its disposal?

- Should external, independent advice be sought?

- What is the experience of the adviser?

- Do they have a track record in this sector?

- Is the board clear about the role of Region and the Treasury?

- Does the board understand the requirements and the impact it may have on time scales?

- Does the board understand the impact on the new organisation's balance sheet?

- Does the board fully understand the legal implications, the role of the Treasury and the responsibility to Parliament?

- Is the board agreed?

25. Does the board understand the impact of guidance on merger proposals?

Guidance on mergers is complicated and the process has to comply with legislation, Treasury requirements and government objectives. The guidance may be difficult for even in-house experts to understand. And it sometimes changes. A thorough understanding of the rules of engagement in the process is vital and every member of the board has a personal responsibility to understand what is going on. It is not enough to say 'I am not an accountant and therefore I leave it to those who understand.' The board is responsible, as a team, to make decisions based on knowledge, understanding and best advice. The board will need to take time, and members must be prepared to say when they find something difficult to understand.

- How will the board create an environment that enables members to admit they do not understand something, without feeling foolish?
- How can the board be sure it really understands the impact of guidance and what it is being asked to do?
- How can the board evaluate the options?
- Who will devise the financial project plan?
- How will board members who do not find financial issues easy be kept up to date?
- Can technical language be 'dejargonised'?
- Who will provide the advice to the board?
- Who is the board's interface at Region and the Treasury?
- Is the finance director up to the task?
- Does everyone fully understand the procedures and responsibilities?
- Can they be explained to the non-financial literate?
- Does the board understand the Treasury and Parliament's involvement?

26. Are there different professional cultures and what, or who, will prevail?

If an organisation has departments it will have 'cultures'. The finance department will see solutions in terms of numbers, HR departments in terms of people. Secondary services may not see a future grounded in primary services and institutional workers may not relish working in the outside world. Age, training and experience all contribute to culture. Culture can turn into tribalism and tribalism into anarchy. Mergers can emphasise cultural differences. The pace at which an organisation works will vary from place to place. Communication adds to the complexity; some departments are more open than others. Some professions have their approach grounded in history, custom and practice; others are quite the opposite. The differences will be highlighted by merger and change. Who prevails in the 'culture battle' will set the tone of the emerging organisation.

- Can differing professional cultures be identified?
- What is their impact on merger delivery?
- How?
- Does it matter?
- Do they work against team working and working together?
- What is in place to encourage team working?

27. Can you create a climate where people will admit 'we have not done that very well'?

This is often the key to successful change management. Organisations that are successful and good at everything they do seldom need to consider merger. Precisely because organisations have weaknesses they need to consider change. Persuading staff that what they are doing is not the best can be difficult. Professional sensibilities, pride, self-esteem are all at stake. In the best of well-run organisations, from time to time, mistakes will occur. The important thing is to learn from them. There is no great sin in getting something wrong; the sin is not knowing something has gone wrong, or worse still, covering it up.

• Do you have a non-blame culture in your organisation – is it OK to make mistakes?

• Are you the kind of organisation that likes to learn?

• How do you create an atmosphere of honesty and openness?

• Can you bench-mark activity, with other organisations, to highlight the strength or weakness of what you do?

• What attempts are there to keep up with best practice?

28. How will you assess the new service configuration?

Mergers mean change, change to pretty well everything. Whatever the reasons that have brought merger on to the agenda – it means change. Services will be reconfigured and control of the reconfiguration process is very important. Some will use a merger to build an empire, others will take the opportunity to demolish someone else's. A clear picture of what the service reconfiguration looks like, its structure and shape, has to be settled early on. The reconfiguration should be assessed against the benefits to patients. The benefits may not be direct, they may be indirect, in as much as infrastructure services to GPs or in-house services may be faster or in some way improved. Whatever the changes a clear understanding of what the end object looks like is pivotal.

- Who will decide reconfiguration really does improve services for patients?

- Will the doctors decide?

- Can you involve the views of patients and special interest groups?

- How can you connect with the local community to see what they want?

- Is Region forcing the issue and are patients getting left behind?

- Can discrete areas of service be translated into 'core business' sectors?

- Are they viable?

- Are the reconfigurations in line and synchronised with your commissioners' priorities?

- How flexible is the reconfiguration model to meet changing demands?

- Are the plans affordable?

29. What are the leadership arrangements?

The leadership arrangements of any merger are crucial to its success and it will be important to clarify them early in the process. The interim board arrangements, particularly agreeing the chair designate, the roles of existing chief executives and the proposed project leadership, will all require early resolution. It will be important to communicate these arrangements to everyone in the organisation and to recognise that it will not be sensible to leave these key decisions until after formal consultation.

- What are the processes for agreeing interim leadership arrangements?
- Will these be joint arrangements?
- Who will decide them?
- What is the role of Region?
- How quickly will you decide?
- What will happen in the interim?
- What permanent arrangements will you make?
- By whom?
- When will key board appointments be made by the shadow board?

30. How will the chair-designate be appointed?

The chair is appointed by the Secretary of State through the regional office, and there are publicly accountable selection processes with independent assessors. It can no longer be seen as 'jobs for the boys'. Emphasis is being placed on 'localness' and the individual's 'commitment' to the NHS – taken to mean no dependence on private medical care. Expertise in running large and complex organisations is vital. Work to identify the chair (and NEDs) (non-executive directors) can begin at any stage before the establishment of new Trusts. This includes advertising and sifting and interviewing potential candidates in line with the appointment procedures at regional office. Ministers can be asked to agree, in principle, to the appointment of a chair for a new Trust in advance of its establishment. But any proposal to ministers must be carefully worded to ensure that the consultation on Trust proposals is not prejudiced. When the Trust has been established a shadow board can be formed and formal letters of appointment can then be sent by ministers. The appointments can be for up to four years but more usually two.

- How do the future plans of the existing Trust chairs impact on the success of the merger?

- What are their current terms of appointment?

- Are they interested in becoming the chair of the new Trust?

- What is the time-scale?

- Will there be adverts in national papers?

- Who will set up the selection process for the formal appointment?

- How does the organisation manage in the meantime?

- Will there be an unmanageable vacuum?

31. How will the new CEO be appointed?

The appointment of a new CEO will be crucial to the success of the new organisation. It is important for this process to be set up as soon as possible to avoid uncertainty and reduce low morale. The identification of the new profile and key objectives for this major leadership role will be critical and will take careful planning. Once quorate the shadow Trust Board can nominate the chief executive of the new Trust who can be appointed once the new Trust is formally appointed.

- What is the selection process?

- Has the Regional Director nominated their external assessor?

- Can a person of suitable experience be found to be an assessor?

- How and who will chose your external assessor?

- Who will brief the assessors and when?

- To what extent are you prepared to let the Regional Assessor influence the decision?

- When will it take place, how important is timing?

- Who will appoint?

- Where there are existing post-holders who meet the specification do you wish to consider an appointment without open competition, using limited internal competition in accordance with EL(97)84?

- Will you use head-hunters?

- What are the interim arrangements for existing CEOs?

- Who will be the merger project manager?

- What are the current contractual arrangements of the existing CEOs?

- Are there cost implications?

- Who pays?

- What are their likely future plans?

32. How will you establish a merger project team?

To facilitate the implementation of any merger requires clearly identified project management and leadership. It will require the ownership and support of all the boards involved and will require nominated individuals who can be released from their current responsibilities, or seconded, or professional advisers appointed as appropriate.

- Who will appoint the project team and project leader?
- Will it be a joint appointment?
- What are the appointments processes?
- When and for how long?
- What are the reporting and accountability arrangements?
- What are the communication channels?

33. What are the arrangements for displaced executives?

Mergers inevitably lead to redundancy or the displacement of some key executives. It is essential that this is planned for sensitively and fairly, and giving equal opportunities for all key players to take part in an open selection process. Some of the executives likely to be displaced will be expected to play an enthusiastic part in creating the foundations of the new organisation. This is asking a great deal of them and of their supervisors. Career development and future training and development opportunities should be available.

- What are the selection processes for all executive posts?

- Who decides?

- What is the time-scale?

- Who will select?

- Will these posts be externally advertised?

- What are the contractual arrangements for all affected executives?

- What are the financial implications?

- What are your personnel policies to deal with displacement?

- What are your redundancy policies?

- What career development and support will you offer to deposed executives?

- Can you offer secondments?

- Or does that put off the 'evil day'?

34. How will other members of staff react to their colleagues leaving?

Research into private sector mergers seems to indicate that key members of staff might 'jump ship' following mergers. Part of the difficulty is created when staff leave the organisation and then encourage their former colleagues to join them. This is particularly true of senior staff who leave and then try to recreate a former team of colleagues in the now organisation.

- How will staff who remain after the merger be reassured?

- Can staff be encouraged to stay by meeting their development needs or offering promotion or new responsibilities?

- Is the answer to keeping staff new ways of working, such as flexi-time?

- Is the 'grass' really 'greener'? Will wavering staff be helped to analyse the benefits of staying or going?

- Is it realistic to persuade someone to stay in an organisation?

- Is there a contract of employment issue to be dealt with?

- If staff are feeling unsettled, what can the organisation do to protect itself from unwanted and predatory head hunters?

35. How will the project team appoint professional advisers?

Depending on the expertise of the current boards it may be unnecessary to appoint professional advisers. Although in some areas it may be crucial, especially to offer independent advice and expertise around new organisational structures and procedures, legal and estates topics are often the areas that require most external input.

- Have you defined the expertise required to successfully implement the merger?

- Will it be required by the project team?

- Who will pay for it?

- Who will check that large contracts, over the European contracting limit, will be advertised in the *European Journal*?

- What are the costs and time delays?

- Who will draw up the specification and contractual arrangements?

- How will they be selected?

- How will you evaluate their expertise and experience?

- What assessment can be undertaken to establish the expertise required by the new organisation?

- If there are deficiencies – will you appoint or buy-in?

36. What will be the business planning process for the new board?

The new organisation will need to develop a new planning process to meet its new needs and it will need to ensure that it reflects the service direction. How will managers and the board ensure that it is an effective process and not just a paper exercise?

- What is the corporate business process for the new organisation?

- Is it a devolved or centralised process?

- Is it understood and owned by the organisation?

- What are the consultation processes?

- What is the board's role?

- What induction and training is required?

- Does it involve commissioners and reflect their priorities?

- How will it be tested?

- Who will lead the process?

- Is it accurately costed and will it be affordable?

- Can it be reviewed?

37. Does the new board understand the impact of changes in commissioning arrangements?

The board of the newly merged organisation will need to identify all its commissioners and carefully review its working arrangements and develop any new relationships that are required as quickly as possible. The board may be populated with 'late arrivers' to the scene and may be unaware of important nuances and historical relationships. A new board is a good opportunity to wipe the slate clean and equally it has a potential to tread on toes.

- Who are your commissioners?
- How many are there?
- Does the organisation have the infrastructure to meet them all regularly?
- How will you establish the commissioners' priority needs?
- What does the organisation do to build relationships with all its commissioners including GPs ?
- Is there a regular method of working and communicating with them?
- Who leads with these working arrangements?
- Will non-executive directors be involved and how?

38. How will the new board develop relationships with all its key commissioner stakeholders?

Before the merger process gets underway, informal discussions with commissioners to seek their views on what is proposed and the impact it might have on their ability to fund service developments and changes are essential. Indeed, the approach may come from commissioners. The new organisation will need to review and evaluate its relationships with all its purchasers and local commissioners. It will need to agree and develop effective working relationships with regular dialogue with all local stakeholders and this includes GPs and Social Services.

- What are relationships like with all purchasers?
- What will you do to improve them?
- What arrangements will be set up to ensure regular dialogue?
- Who will lead the process?
- What will be the role of the new board?
- Do board members develop informal links with commissioners?
- Are the formal arrangements meaningful and do they produce results?
- Are they a talk shop?
- How do things 'get done' with commissioners?

39. What other agencies will you want to involve?

Experience has shown that you need to involve a range of key stakeholders in developing the merger proposals, not only to gain support but also for future joint working. It may be beneficial to include some of these organisations or individuals on your project team, particularly if you are offering community or social care or planning a reconfiguration of any services.

- Who are your stakeholders?
- Who are the organisations you need to involve and consult with throughout the merger process?
- What will be their roles?
- How will you communicate with them?
- Who will you want to include in your project team arrangements?
- At what level should the approach be made and the joint planning be established?

40. What is the role of Social Services – how will you involve them?

Any proposed changes in service delivery will certainly involve Social Services as partners in care. Depending on the nature of the Trusts considering a merger, Social Services are likely to be key players and if there are pilot projects in the pipeline, for example in primary care, then it could also be important to involve them at project team and at board level.

- What are your current joint arrangements with Social Services?

- Are the personal relationships good?

- Do you have joint teams?

- What are the implications of the proposed merger on joint working with Social Services?

- How will these be dealt with?

- What will be the consultation arrangements?

- How will they be involved?

- Who will be involved and at what level?

- Will they be invited to joint the relevant project groups?

41. In the pre-merger phase, how will you organise joint working?

Joint working with outside organisations such as Social Services and others plays a pivotal role in the provision of modern health care. Bringing organisations together may not mean an end to existing arrangements. Geography and local authority boundaries may mean different organisations to work with and the creation of new partnerships.

* Will the joint working arrangements change on reconfiguration?
* Are working practices the same or will systems have to be developed to accommodate the differences?
* Can joint working partners be persuaded to change what they do to allow for streamlined, single style working?
* Will staff need extra familiarisation training?
* Is there a potential for different budgets, in different areas, to produce a two-tier service?

42. How will you handle the consultation process?

The legislation regarding Trusts and possible mergers requires a formal three-month consultation period, which is managed as an independent process by the regional office. However, it is essential to set up regular informal consultation mechanisms which listen to the views of all key stakeholders, including the CHCs, throughout the merger process.

• Who will develop the consultation strategy?

• What is your consultation strategy?

• Is it joint?

• Who will lead it and who will be involved?

• How will you deal with feedback?

• How will you communicate your responses?

43. How will you deal with internal consultation?

Winning the hearts and minds of staff, being honest about the issues and what it means for them and alleviating unnecessary fears are important parts of the merger consultation process. This means setting up regular meetings to listen to staff and to seek their views.

- What are your internal consultation arrangements?
- Will there be similar processes across all organisations?
- What information needs to be shared with whom?
- How often will you hold consultation events with your staff?
- Who will lead the sessions?
- Will there be opportunities for written consultation from staff?
- Do you have the in-house expertise to deal with the issues?
- Should you appoint outside consultants?
- How will they be chosen?
- How will you assess their competence?
- Have they previous success in this sector?
- What are the success criteria?
- Do they understand the NHS?

44. How will you handle external consultation?

Any merger process requires both formal and informal external consultation processes which will require careful planning. The organisations involved will need to set up regular informal consultation arrangements with all key stakeholders. It will not be acceptable to leave everything to the formal consultation process which usually takes place much later, and is handled independently by the regional office. Establishing in the minds of the public that mergers do not mean cuts or closures is a difficult task that will need a great deal of sensitive management attention, and most probably in complex cases or where services are 'much loved' and well established – professional communicators may provide a key to a successful change.

- What will be your external consultation strategy?

- What will be your key messages ?

- Who will be responsible for producing it and leading it?

- What will be the role of the current chairs and chief executives?

- Who will you consult with?

- What will be the informal processes ?

- How will you respond and link in with the formal process run by Region?

- Will you appoint external consultants?

- How will you choose them?

- Do they know about the NHS?

- What is their track record?

- Have they done this type of work before?

- Do they need to be local?

- Is this a PR (public relations) battle that is not winnable?

45. How will you deal with the press and media?

Unless relations with the press and media are carefully and sensitively handled, mergers are almost certain to receive a negative press – that will cascade into the morale of staff and the performance of the organisation. It will be essential to communicate regularly with the press and to identify a spokesperson who can build up a positive relationship with key journalists and give them regular briefings on all the issues. The relationship between the project manager/chief executive and editors of the local press will be important. It is better to be proactive rather than only reactive. Organisations that have a high national or regional profile may expect the attentions of national (if not international) media. Prepare yourself for the onslaught!

- What is your policy on dealing with the media and the press, now?

- Is it effective?

- Do you currently provide informal briefings?

- Will your new-found 'friendships' with the press be regarded as just a way of influencing editors away from the real issues?

- Can you point to good, frank and open relationships in the past?

- Are press relations, arrangements and experience robust enough?

- What is your agreed joint policy during the merger process?

- Can you agree a joint line particularly where there are unwilling partners in the process?

- Who will you deal with locally?

- Who will you deal with nationally?

- Who will lead and work with the press and media on a regular basis?

- Do you need outside consultants to take on part of the work or train your own people?

- How will they be selected?

46. Who is to be the merging organisation's spokesperson?

Effective communication, which involves positive and regular communication with the local community and all interested organisations, in particular with the media and the press, will make the merger a great deal less painful. The appointment of the right person is a crucial decision and will require careful thought. It does not have to be a chair or a chief executive but their relationship with the CEOs and chairs will be very important.

- Who will decide who should be the spokesperson?
- Have you defined the role?
- Will they have open access to the organisations at the highest level?
- Will it be someone within ?
- What are the training needs?
- Unsocial hours come with the territory in this kind of role – will the person be able to cope with the potential for out-of-hours and weekend demands on their time?
- Will you appoint an external expert?
- How will you evaluate their past record?
- Who will they report to?
- Will it be a joint appointment?
- How much will they cost?
- How will it be resourced?

47. Will there be a communications audit for the newly merged organisation?

All organisations communicate in their own way. Some do it well and some have no idea. It will be important for the new organisation to review what has worked and to set up new arrangements that reflect and enhance the culture of the new organisation. An audit of communications will be important.

- Who will undertake it?
- How will you avoid prejudice in the outcome?
- Have merging organisations carried out communications audits?
- What did they reveal?
- What are the successes?
- What are the barriers?
- What can be learned?
- What will the new organisation want to audit?
- Is timing an issue – too early or too late?
- Will it result in a communications strategy?
- Will it be effective?
- How will you know?
- What yardsticks can be developed to measure the improvement in communication impact?

48. How will the newly merged organisation develop an internal communications strategy?

Organisations that have merged and undergone major change will have staff who feel anxious and concerned. Effective communication is the key to smooth change and requires very careful planning. It is not just an add-on and will need to be given a high priority by the new chair and CEO. The organisation will need to develop a communications style that reflects its future direction and is genuinely two-way and promotes listening and sharing. Two-way communication is based on honesty and some answers that the organisation may wish to give managers and board members may not be flattering and not the news you may want to hear. That is exactly the news you must listen to.

- Does the board understand that communication is not just about sending out a monthly news letter?
- Will you develop a new communications strategy?
- What will it include?
- How can you be sure that the components are complementary?
- Who will design and prepare it?
- Who will you involve in the process?
- Will you use outside consultants or experts?
- What type of mapping exercise will you undertake?
- Do you know what you want to say?
- What techniques will you use to say it?
- What will be the barriers to success?
- What will be the role of the chair and CEO?
- Who will ensure implementation?
- What training is needed?
- What will it cost?
- Can the board deal with the reaction that 'the money would be better spent on patients'?
- What are the key outcomes?
- When and how will you review it?

49. How will you involve patient and user groups?

Merging organisations are required to demonstrate the benefits of any changes to patients and service users. They are often criticised for only involving them through the formal consultation process or via the CHC. Regular dialogue with service users is important on a continuous basis, with the focus on making services user-friendly and patient focused. This should not be seen as an additional task by busy managers rather it should be built into the formal and informal communications and feedback mechanisms set up with patients and local user groups in mind.

- How do you propose to involve users and patients?
- What will be the mechanisms and supports?
- How will you ensure it is not just tokenism?
- Will you involve independent advocates for some service users?
- What information and feedback will be set up?
- What will be the role of the board?
- How will you evaluate how user-friendly your services are?
- Is this an in-house task or should outside experts be brought in?

50. Will the composition of the non-executive board members influence the success of the merger?

What is the relationship between the organisation's success and the board's ability to work together as a team? Identifying the right people to work together has far reaching consequences for future success. Never more so than where a merger is concerned. Should the new board be composed of representatives from the outgoing boards? Should there be a clean sweep and a new board appointed? Will there be a choice? The new board will need to demonstrate a range of talents, and getting together the right team is vital. The selection processes mean there may also be entirely new members. Legislation prevents cross membership by NEDs. This gives rise to a requirement for the resignation of some of the NEDs of the original Trust(s), who will become members of the new Trust.

- Will the new board be composed of members from the outgoing organisation?

- Is this wise – will they bring fresh ideas or old baggage?

- Will they really have the time to do the job effectively?

- Do they really understand what is expected of them?

- How can you test that?

- What skills will they contribute?

- How will they be encouraged to work together?

- How will the relationships be tested and developed?

- Can poor performers be encouraged, trained or removed?

51. What are the arrangements for the outgoing boards to work together in the run-up process?

Outgoing board members may have mixed emotions and motives during the merger run-up period. Some will be departing, some will be staying. Some will be forced out and others pressured to stay. Board selection procedures may make it impossible to determine what the new board will look like, it may be a whole new team. How the merging organisations work in the preparatory period could have a serious impact on the success of the emerging organisation. Will they be a harmonious team or will they be warring factions?

- Will the merging boards always meet together?

- Will they meet separately and come together as need dictates?

- If so who will determine 'need'?

- How will responsibility be divided and who leads the process?

- Will parts of each of the boards meet for specific purposes – how will feedback be managed?

- Is one board likely to overshadow another – how can turning a merger into a board room takeover be avoided?

- Will management teams meet together?

- How will the project team interface with the outgoing boards?

- What is the timing for the new shadow board to take over?

52. What is the role of the shadow Trust board?

The shadow Trust exists from the date of formal establishment of the Trust to the operational date, which is normally 1 April. It has a small number of specific functions and roles. Once quorate it may nominate the chief executive of the new Trust and set up its operating processes. It is also able to receive transferred property, enter into NHS contracts and other contracts such as those for the employment of staff.

- What arrangements will you make to set up a shadow board?
- Do you understand the legal requirements?
- What will be the selection process for the shadow board?
- What will be the role of Region and the Secretary of State?
- Who will oversee the selection process?
- What are the resignation requirements for non-executive directors who are required to leave their 'old' Trust before they can be appointed to the new one?
- Will you wish to make arrangements to mark their leaving and their contribution?

53. What are the induction processes for the new board?

The new organisation may bring together components that are very different. Time-served board members will need to get to know the 'new bits' and new members will have a great deal to assimilate. This applies to managers, executive and non-executive directors. All parts of the organisation should be on show, good and bad. After all, nothing gets improved if it is not known to be poor to start with. The 'get to know you' programme needs planning; key people must be available and time set aside.

* Who is responsible for the programme?

* Will visits be formal, allowing for a departmental presentation, or will they be informal and of a 'drop-in' nature?

* How will the induction needs of the board be established?

* Will management induction be different?

* How long will it all take?

* Should visits be announced or unannounced?

* Should the induction be shaped around the availability of the directors or around the organisation?

* Is induction undertaken better in groups or singly?

* Is there need for a senior manager induction programme?

* Would all staff benefit from being able to visit 'new parts' of the organisation?

* Is induction a continuous programme?

* Can executives be 'twinned' with non-executives to reflect special expertise or interest in departmental or service functions?

* Is this desirable – does it reinforce tribalism?

54. How will you assess and use the skills of the new board?

Few would argue there is a relationship between the success of the organisation and the skills of the board members. Getting the right people in the right place at the right time is a great trick to pull off. Selection processes for boards are now much more open than they were. Board members are appointed from a pool of suitable candidates. Careful assessment of their skills and how they can contribute becomes very significant. The process is 'removed' and bureaucratic. Although great emphasis is placed upon such factors as 'localness' there is also the commonsense objective of making sure a team of people can work together.

- Will the non-executives have time to do the job properly?

- Do they really understand the extent of the commitment they are taking on?

- What skills do they have and do they add value to their being there?

- Can they understand the difference between executive and non-executive behaviour?

- What is the relationship between the chairman and the chief executive?

- How will relationships between board members be tested and developed?

- If board members underperform, how can they be trained, encouraged or removed?

- Will executive members be encouraged to reveal their career plans?

- Will good people be encouraged to stay?

- In planning the new board will posts depend on the 'best person for the job', or will thought be given to equal representation from the merging units?

55. How will you ensure the members of the new board work well together?

In any new organisation, learning to work together takes time. In a recently merged organisation, with the attendant potential for friction or stress, the problems can be amplified. Getting away from the organisation, away from its pressures and distractions, is a good way of getting to know one another, learning to understand each other and planing for what is ahead. Sometimes called 'time out' or 'away days', the idea is to focus on the board working together as a team.

* Where is the best place for time out?

* If it is in-house, whose house? Which of the merger partners will provide the venue, or is neutral territory a better bet?

* If the venue is elsewhere, will it be properly equipped with everything you might need (overhead projectors, flip charts etc)?

* Can you agree a date that suits everyone? Time out doesn't work well if someone is missing.

* Who will develop the aims of the meeting?

* Who will arrange and agree the agenda?

* Can everyone have a say in agreeing the agenda?

* How long will 'time out' last? Longer than you estimate for the first session!

* Will the agenda allow for groups to work together as well as plenary sessions?

* Who will be the facilitator?

* Where will they come from?

* Who will brief them?

* Will you ask for a report?

* How often will you do it?

* What is the budget and who will pay?

* How will you evaluate the benefits?

56. How will you ensure that the new organisation's board meetings will work?

'Time out' and efforts to build a team go some way to making boards work. In merger situations members of outgoing boards can take some time to shed 'old ways' and acquire new ones. The first few meetings might show members jockeying for position or establishing their credentials. Regular meetings can become dull and uninspiring. For the organisation to work, board meetings and their members have to work.

- Does the chair understand the pivotal role to play in melding two organisations into one?

- Is any training required?

- Is previous experience relevant?

- Are the meetings a rubber stamp?

- Does the meeting-cycle fit the needs of the organisation or the needs of members?

- How does the board know the information that reaches it is reliable, well judged and sound?

- Does the board hear what it wants to hear or does it go out of its way to be 'told it like it really is'?

- Do pre-meetings take place? Should they?

- How is genuine debate encouraged?

- How does the board measure success?

57. How do you propose to choose the name of the new Trust?

Does the name of the new organisation matter? Sometimes, for reasons of history, local connections or respect for what has gone before, organisations can have a strong attachment to their name. Sensitivities about names can become a festering resentment if they are peremptorily overlooked. A new name, reflecting the new nature of the successor organisation, might be the answer – but that needs careful consideration too. 'What's in a name?' Should the name reflect the geography of the area or the nature of the services?

- What are the sensitivities around name issues?
- How will the name be chosen?
- Do the nature of the services have to be announced in the name – is it wise or desirable to include 'mental health' or other generic descriptions in the title of the organisation?
- Does it matter?
- Should it matter?
- How can sensitivities be assessed?
- Is it wise for the 'new' name to be a hybrid of the 'old' names?
- Is a ballot a good idea – could you be left with a name, popular now, but one which will not stand the test of time?
- Who will have a say in the naming process?
- Who has the final decision?
- Is the name the logo – or is that a separate issue?

58. How does meeting in public affect debate and decision making?

Recent changes in regulations now bring Trusts under the provisions of the Public Bodies (Admissions to Meetings) Act 1960. This will not be a challenge for the many Trusts who already hold some of their meetings in public. For others it may define a whole new way of working. An organisation facing change will have to take great care in how it deals with some of the more sensitive issues around merger and change.

- Who will brief the board on the provisions of the 1960 Act?

- Are they competent to interpret it?

- Can advice be sought from Trusts who already meet in public?

- How can items dealing with such issues as workforce downsizing and departmental closures or restructuring be discussed without stampeding staff or public opinion before a decision has been taken?

- What items will be reserved for discussion in private?

- Who decides?

- Will board members 'play to the gallery' if the public and press are present?

- Will Trusts' standing orders have to be revised?

- Is where you meet now suitable for members of the public to attend and be seated comfortably?

- Will you need a new venue?

- In the organisation or outside of it? Is there adequate access and facilities for the disabled?

- How will you announce times and venues of your meetings?

- Will agendas be published for the public and press in advance of the meeting?

- Will you vary the meeting venue to give everyone a chance to attend?

- Will it change the way in which agenda items are written?

59. How will the new board set its agenda for meetings?

Mechanisms for allowing items to find their way on to the agenda do vary from organisation to organisation. A merged organisation will have to review those processes. Who will plan the agenda? What regard does there have to be now that Trusts are obliged to meet in public? Who decides what goes on to the agenda and why? Some items will be regular and reported month on month to highlight variations and trends; others will be one-off. Will the agenda keep the Board in touch with what is really happening in the organisation?

- Who will be responsible for compiling the agenda?
- Who will have the final say?
- How will deadlines be fixed for including agenda items?
- Is there provision for urgent items?
- Does the agenda allow for informal discussion?
- Will agendas be 'pre-published' for the press and public?
- Will the board meet before the public meeting?
- Can financial information be presented graphically or in such a way that the public and non-finance people can understand it?
- How will regular items be bench-marked to show progress?
- How will the items on the agenda be evaluated – do they really address the real issues?
- Can a balance be struck over reactive and active agenda items?
- How much appears on the agenda? Is it limited to a certain number of items?
- How long should a meeting last? Is it time barred?
- Should the agenda be split into items for decision, discussion and information?
- Can the agenda dissolve the differences between merged organisations or would it be better to deal with merged organisations separately to satisfy their particular needs?
- Is there an option to use IT to make board presentations easier and can agendas be circulated to members on disc or by e-mail?

60. Will the new board need special support mechanisms?

Board members need agendas and supporting paper work. In a merged organisation where some of the issues may be unfamiliar the need for background material may increase. Who will provide it and how much time will it take up? A new board may give an opportunity for a new approach. Can the management of information by the use of technology be used to advantage?

- Does the board have dedicated secretarial support or is it just one part of someone's job.

- Will all the documents be on paper or is it possible to provide data on disc or via e-mail?

- Is there a need for a 'company secretary'?

- Who will minute the work of the board?

- Who verifies the minutes?

- When will minutes be circulated and who by?

- Can it be done electronically?

- Is it worth supplying members with the necessary PCs or software to make better use of technology?

- Who schedules non-executives' time? Trust HQ or 'outside offices'?

- What are the working relationships?

61. Will the board understand new and more complex financial information?

A merged organisation almost certainly means a bigger organisation. Bigger begets complexity. Board members confess that often the most difficult part of their job is understanding financial information. Finance information does not have to be pages of numbers. It can be presented in a form that allows for performance comparisons and key indicators.

- Has the board decided what financial information it needs?
- Are board meeting schedules and monthly out-turn information synchronised?
- Will information be presented in a consistent way?
- Will financial information be integrated with other performance measures?
- Will the board be able to digest the information?
- Is some training required?
- Has the board agreed upon the method and style of the presentation it requires?
- Who interprets the information?
- Are the numbers presented as graphs and charts?
- Is there a narrative?
- Is it meaningful?
- How will the board be sure the information reflects the true position?

62. How accessible is the new board?

The Board is not an extension of the executive – it instructs the executive. Nevertheless, it is important for the board to be close enough to the organisation to recognise what is wrong and what is right about its performance. A new board will be a new phenomenon to the staff and the board has to decide how accessible it is to the staff. After all it is the staff who are responsible for implementing the board's decisions and whose careers and future will be affected by these decisions. Where redundancies and lay-offs have been part of the merger process the board may think it vital to get close to the organisation as soon as possible.

• Do the staff know who the board members are?

• Are the board recognised by the staff?

• Do they know their names?

• What opportunity do they have to meet?

• Do board members appear to be privileged, by having dedicated parking places or reserved places in the canteen or dining room?

• Should they?

• Do the staff think the board adds value to the organisation?

• How do you know the answer?

• Is there a planned programme of board visits to all parts of the Trust?

• Are drop-in visits made?

• What is achieved by visits?

63. How will the new board communicate its decisions and how accessible will it be?

It will be particularly important for the new board of a newly merged organisation to be both visible and accessible. Its availability to staff and the public will be a test of its commitment to openness and transparency in decision making. Effective team briefing sessions following board meetings are also essential.

- How will the board publicise its programme of meetings and to whom?

- Will meetings be in the boardroom or will they be held across the organisation?

- Will staff members be encouraged to attend and how?

- Will a summary of board meetings be available and widely published?

- How will the management team be briefed about the decisions of the board and how fast?

- Will there be planned board visits and informal communication events?

- Will the board members want to be recognised by staff and how will they achieve this?

64. What is the vision of the new organisation?

A merger will have been put in place to achieve certain objectives. Improved services, future security or saving money are some of the principal reasons. Beyond that the new organisation has to define its purpose. The purpose needs to be a shared direction, something all the staff believe in and respect. A simple statement of aims or values can unite organisations around a common purpose.

• Will the organisation express its values and aims?

• What can be done to ensure all staff can play a part in defining the purpose?

• Will contributions be individual or departmental, or both?

• Who takes the lead in the process?

• Who will sponsor it at board level?

• How will the purpose be communicated within the organisation?

• How will the purpose be communicated outside the organisation?

65. How will the new board win people over?

All the evidence from mergers in the private sector and in the NHS points to the fact that staff go through a period of great uncertainty. Many good staff will jump ship, and following a merger some data points to the fact that 18 per cent of senior managers seek employment elsewhere. The board has to put itself into a position where it wins the trust of employees and moves quickly to win over the doubters and consolidate the workforce.

- Does the board recognise the problem?

- Who will be the board sponsor for any action that needs to be taken?

- Is an organisation wide-programme required or is it only in some parts or among some grades that action needs to be taken?

- How approachable is the board?

- Do board members go out of their way to meet with and talk to staff?

- Are there any quick fixes that the board can make to demonstrate good faith?

- How will the board share its long-term plans?

- How can the organisation be part of shaping the plans?

- Can the board give a realistic answer to the question 'why should anyone want to work here'?

66. What will remind the board that it is there to serve residents, patients and clients?

In large or complex organisations undergoing great change, it is easy for the leaders to become fixed on managerial and process issues and overlook the fact that the purpose of the organisation is to provide services for 'customers' – residents, patients and clients. Staying connected with the service is an important part of delivering a smooth merger programme. It is also encouraging for staff to see that mergers and change are not just about money but they are service driven, too.

- What mechanisms are in place for the board to stay in touch with the opinions and needs of its 'customers'.
- How often does the board meet with voluntary and patient representative groups?
- Does the board visit service delivery areas of the organisation?
- Can the board demonstrate it has responded to 'customer' demand?
- Are there any market research mechanisms to inform the board of 'customer' reaction and demand?
- How does the board bench-mark its success?

67. How will values play their part in shaping the culture of the new organisation?

A newly merged organisation may be unsure of itself. Emerging perhaps from the uncertainties of redundancies and reorganisation, messages can be ambiguous and the future poorly defined for staff. This is not a recipe for getting the best out of people. Can values play a part?

• How will you overcome cynicism that a statement of purpose is just another set of words on the notice-board?

• How do you achieve ownership and commitment?

• How will the organisation test itself against its statement of purpose?

• How will the board assess whether the organisation is living up to its ambitions?

• Will the purpose be revisited and refreshed, as time passes?

• What is the process?

• Can a new culture be developed?

• How do you move the organisation beyond just being a place to go to work?

68. How will the new organisation go about merging operational policies?

Is it necessary for the new organisation, the product of two or more Trusts, to replicate operational policy throughout the new organisation, particularly if they occupy different sites? On the other hand might it be infinitely preferable, if not vital, to create a whole raft of new policies for a new organisation?

- Who will evaluate the policies?
- Who will define what is good and can you avoid 'throwing the baby out with the bathwater'?
- Do pay and reward strategies match throughout the new organisation?
- If not, is there a cost attached to harmonisation?
- Are the skill mixes the same?
- Are there differential issues in managerial pay structures?
- Do administrative policies match?
- In what sense are there duplications and how can they be avoided?
- What is the mechanism for auditing policies?
- What are the mechanisms to supplant policies as older ones get refreshed or time expired?
- Will the most up-to-date policy be the one that is followed?
- How will you overcome departmental resistance to new polices and the 'we have always done it this way' attitude?
- What are the training requirements?
- How will criteria be developed to ensure the emerging policies meet the needs of the new organisation?
- Will they be robust enough for the future, or are they interim?
- Should they be?
- Is it possible to define all the policies at one go?
- Are trade union and staff side organisations meeting structures the same?
- Are major incident policies the same?

69. Will a risk management assessment be undertaken for the new entity?

All enterprises carry risk, and health services, because of the special work they do, can be exposed to considerable risk. Risks as employers, risks as service suppliers, risks to visitors. The prospects are endless. Bringing organisations together may wipe out some risks and introduce others. A risk assessment analysis is also a formal requirement of the application for merger process.

- How soon can work start on a risk management audit?
- Is risk management part of the merger strategy?
- Who takes a lead?
- Is risk management part of a quality strategy?
- Who will evaluate the clinical risks?
- Do operating procedures invite or limit risks?
- Are health and safety policies up to date?
- What are the financial risks?
- Is it wise to have the risks evaluated in-house or should the full range of risks be assessed by an outside organisation?
- What is the cost of this?
- Are there resources to pay for it?
- How will the assessors be selected?
- When did the component organisations last have a visit from the Health and Safety Inspectorate?
- What are the risks related to software? Is it all licensed?
- Are there procedures for keeping up to date with changes in legislation, including European Union requirements?
- How can the board be certain the organisation is not running unnecessary risks?
- What is the medical director's role in managing risk?
- How will the board develop a comprehensive risk management strategy?

70. How will the new management structure be designed?

Mergers are likely to leave a mark on management and their structures. Some posts will disappear and duplication will be avoided. Not all organisations manage themselves in the same way. In one place duties may be the preserve of senior managers and in others more junior managers will be encouraged to cope. Style, service configuration and geography can all play a part in management structure. There are often strong indications that changes will have to be made.

- Will the structure fit around the needs of the organisation or will the organisation be changed by the managerial structure?
- Is a management audit part of the merger strategy?
- How much overlap is there?
- What is the impact?
- Is the structure 'flat' or hierarchical?
- Is the structure task oriented?
- Can the style be defined?
- Are competencies matched?
- Are there training and development needs?
- Do the structures allow for career advancement?
- What is the impact on managers' motivation?
- What does managerial productivity mean to the board?
- What does it mean to managers and their careers?

71. Are there differences in management style to be overcome?

Organisations can develop their own personality and much of their character will come from the style adopted by the managers. Some management styles encourage openness, others are more centralist. Some organisations are more disciplined than others; some are financially driven and others are medically driven. Some are relaxed and some are formal. Bringing organisations together requires an understanding of the character, colour and texture of management and the extent to which management styles will have to be reconciled.

- Can differences in management style be determined?

- Are senior managers and board members addressed by their first names?

- Is the internal disciplinary record of the organisation a good way to assess style?

- How accessible are managers?

- Is all contact formal?

- Is there room for management by 'huddle'?

- How open is management?

- Do they admit their misjudgments?

- How will the management style interface with the needs of the new organisation?

- Will style lead the organisation or will the organisation be led with 'style'?

72. What are the most important issues that have to be dealt with?

Managing mergers and change can be a frenetic business. Deadlines have to be reconciled and other issues must be in place from day one. How are the priorities determined? There will be formal processes to be considered and planned for – much of which is prescribed in 'guidance'. There will also be 'hearts and minds' issues that are just as important. The tougher the decision, the more likely it is that it will have an impact on people and their futures. The issues are interrelated. There is no 'list', just a host of issues that are intertwined.

- Can you step back from the organisation and assess issue prioritisation?
- If there don't seem to be too many issues, should you check again?
- Are the main issues 'people issues'?
- Are there too many or too few?
- Is the financial information robust enough to be relied upon?
- Do some services have to be closed or downsized?
- What are the service quality issues?
- What is the relationship with the commissioners?
- What services will they continue to fund?
- What are the long range and short range objectives?

73. How can the new organisation develop a good relationship with the performance team at Region?

It will be important to work closely with Region before, during and after the merger. There is a series of formal processes required for any proposed merger which requires the support of Region from the initial expression of interest, through the consultation process and to the final approval stage. It is the regional office who must prepare a submission to ministers and this involves a full option appraisal prepared by the project team. Following a merger it will be the performance team at the Region office who will monitor the relevant business plans.

- Are there any skeletons in the cupboard?
- Who will lead on performance monitoring ?
- What is their experience?
- Does the organisation have the skill-sets required to work with Region?
- What processes will be set up?
- What will be the informal and formal processes with the performance team?
- How good are the communications?
- How will the board be involved?

74. What is the impact on estates issues?

Mergers may bring together organisations that have neighbouring estates or perhaps those that are far apart. Evaluating the worth of estates, retaining it, using it on a lease basis or disposing of part of it is a complex and time consuming job.

- Do you own the estate or do you rent it?
- Do you want to change that position, on merger?
- Do you have an estates department?
- Is the job best done 'out-of-house'?
- Is the estate department up to the job?
- How will the estate be valued?
- If there are disposals, who will handle them?
- How will they be chosen?
- What time-scale is acceptable?
- What is the allowance for slippage in the programme?
- Who will assess the market and decide the best time to move?
- What is the state of repair of the building stock?
- Are there cost implications?
- If construction is planned, what is the Local Authority's position, what are the planning implications?
- Is the full cost of planning, legal and professional fees built into the budget?
- What are the PFI (private finance initiative) issues?

75. Can the new organisation reduce its capital charges?

A merger may be a good time to have a ruthless look at the building stock. Is it all required and how can an opportunity be created to reduce capital charges?

- Do you know what the capital charges to the new organisation will be?

- What is your future investment or disinvestment strategy?

- Are all buildings and land required?

- Should the new organisation rent its estate?

- Can relocation be arranged in such a way as to release land and buildings in discrete parcels?

- Can buildings not required but not ready for disposal be decommissioned in such a way as to avoid capital charges?

- Does the new organisation need all the items which carry a capital charge?

- Is there a disposal programme?

76. How will the new human resource agenda be delivered?

A new human resource agenda will be required for the new organisation and it will be essential to recognise the organisational and cultural differences. They will apply to any differences between the terms and conditions of service for staff and different policies and procedures.

- How will the new board translate its human resource strategy into a real agenda?

- What is the HR capacity of the new organisation?

- Is it able to meet its new needs?

- What are the priority issues and how will they be handled?

- What are the differences that will need reconciling?

77. What are the implications for staff in the new organisation?

As part of the application and consultation process the project team will be required to set out the implications for all staff across the merging organisations. This will include a human resources strategy which sets out the future direction of the new Trust and any staffing issues. It will be essential to plan and discuss these implications with all relevant groups of staff throughout the merger process and prior to formal consultation.

- What are your future plans for staff?
- Do they reflect the needs of the reconfigured services?
- Will there be redundancies?
- If so, what are your policies for dealing with them?
- Can they be financed?
- Where does this fit in with the future human resource direction?
- What are the implications in terms of people?
- What are the implications in terms of costs?

78. How will new members of staff be introduced to the organisation?

For any newly merged organisation it will be important not only to think about how existing staff will learn to work together in positive ways but also how new staff are introduced. Mergers sometimes leave in their wake an affection for what has gone before that can translate itself into tribalism or cliques in the new. Stories abound and 'the good old days' are an important part of recognising the past but can be formidable to new staff who feel they are 'on the outside'. Integration can become an issue. This will be key to positive recruitment and retention as new members of staff will always remember how they were first treated.

- How will you make new staff feel welcome?

- What will you do for new live-in staff?

- Will they have 'welcome buddies'?

- Who will support younger members of staff?

- What helpful information will they receive in advance?

- What form will induction take?

- Is there a specific getting-started course?

- Is it relevant, user-friendly and timely?

- Will it apply to all staff including doctors and others on rotation?

- Will new staff meet key senior staff and board members?

- Will they understand the vision and values of the organisation and share them?

- Will they evaluate the meet-and-greet programme?

- How will it be followed up and changed if necessary?

79. How will you reassure staff about their futures?

Staff in merging organisations will feel threatened and uncertain about their futures. Staff who are at risk will be more worried about their futures than they will about performing at work. Expect sickness levels to rise and complaints to increase. If you can reassure staff, then it is important to give positive and reassuring messages. If staff are at risk, then it is important to be honest and establish fair procedures for dealing with this; through open and equitable selection processes, retraining plans, and agreed redundancy policies where necessary.

- What analysis has been undertaken around future staffing requirements?
- What discussions have there been with affected staff groups and their representatives?
- What policies have been agreed around these issues?
- Do you have agreed redundancy policies and procedures?
- What are the implications?
- How much will this cost?
- Are there alternative strategies around retraining?
- Are there career development opportunities for affected staff?
- What is the cost?
- Is there a central clearing house with other Trusts and agencies?
- Can you offer secondments?
- What are you doing to keep key staff?

80. How can staff costs be reduced without cutting staff or reducing services?

The battle for the future of the NHS will be fought against cost and value for money. The efficiency indices for the NHS are being reviewed and *more for less* becomes a by-word. There appears little appetite for increasing taxes to fund the NHS and politicians are fearful of introducing the prospect of patient co-payment. For the forseeable future, more for less is the only answer. Over 70 per cent of NHS costs are accounted for in wages and salaries. This is a key issue for the new organisation and its success will be around how effective it can be in introducing credible performance systems that are understood and owned by all staff in the organisation.

- Are the financial and performance management systems linked?
- How effective are they?
- How do they link to the organisation's objectives?
- How devolved are contracting and budgetary systems?
- Do key clinicians and managers of staff and clinical resources manage and understand these budgets?
- Do they own and want responsibility?
- Do they have training needs?
- Do they have timely information about all expenditure against their budgets ?
- What are the unplanned absences statistics?
- Is sickness and absence carefully monitored and how?
- Is annual leave carefully managed to avoid excess overtime and cover costs?
- What is the state of morale?
- What are your turnover rates?
- What is the cost of your recruitment in terms of time and money?
- What could you do to retain staff?
- Do you have exit interviews?
- Do the board monitor them?
- What are they telling you?

81. Can the board afford to be honest about job losses?

If the merger is the result of the need to make cost reductions then this will inevitably have an impact on staff. It will be essential to prepare staffing assumptions in advance and continuous dialogue with all staff groups and their staff representatives is of the utmost importance. One-to-one discussions with staff potentially at risk are also important along with opportunities for alternative employment, retraining or career support and advice. You cannot expect staff whose future is under threat to make a positive contribution to the organisation at one of the most critical phases in its history.

- What are the staffing implications for the new organisation?
- Are the assumptions viable in the longer term?
- Have staff potentially at risk been identified?
- What discussions and arrangements have been agreed?
- Who will lead these discussions?
- What HR policies have been agreed to deal with affected staff?
- What support mechanisms will be set up for staff at risk?
- Have you left enough time for one-to-one counselling?
- Do you have career counsellors on hand?
- What is the cost implication?
- What is the cost of redundancies and retraining, counselling etc?
- Can Trusts in your Region set up a staff employment 'bank' to help transition?
- Can staff who want to leave to take up a career as a management consultant be helped to 'go-solo'?
- Do they have a realistic chance of success?
- Who will identify their skills?

82. Is there a likelihood of industrial action?

In any re-organisation it is essential to establish good working relationships with trade unions and staff organisations. Industrial relations are likely to be at their most sensitive at times of change. What will you do to ensure good relations and to prevent the possibility of any industrial action?

* Are there any unresolved disputes, disconnected with the merger, that might sour the merger and need to be dealt with first?
* What is the industrial relations climate in the merging organisations?
* Are your staff organisations in support of the merger?
* What have you done to work with them on unresolved issues?
* Are there regular communications channels?
* What are your formal and informal links?
* What is the trade union's national position – does it vary from the local stance?

83. Do you have contingency plans in the event of an industrial dispute?

Industrial disputes following a merger do not give positive messages about the relations with staff in the new organisation but can be expected and are more difficult to manage. It will be important to ask what could have been done differently and how the dispute can be resolved quickly and fairly. It will be important to plan for such an event and to seriously consider the reputation of the new organisation. Preoccupation with merger-mania can lead to a lack of sensitivity and clumsy decisions can get an organisation into trouble. It is not unknown for staff side organisations to exploit mergers, to improve conditions of service, to buy co-operation. Is this likely and can you afford to give in? Today's decision may be one to regret in the long run.

- Why has a dispute come about?
- What could have been done to avoid it?
- What is the relationship with staff organisations?
- What could have been done differently?
- What are your contingency plans if there is a dispute?
- Who will it affect?
- Are patients at risk?
- Could it have been avoided?
- What next for industrial relations in the new organisation?

84. How does job design play its part in the future?

If the new organisation is facing a range of recruitment and retention issues or needs to embark on job reprofiling then job design can play a helpful and important role. It can be a valuable part of a skill-mix and reprofiling programme. Modern health care is about fitting the skills of the individuals around the service needs of the patient. The days when patients had to fit into the hospital's regime are gone. The trend will be towards 'consumerism' in health care where the patient is increasingly recognised as a 'customer'.

* How will you use job design to improve services?

* How does it fit in with organisational audit?

* Will it apply across the organisation or only to certain areas?

* Who will undertake job design?

* Will staff be able to design their own jobs?

* Who will keep job design fair and up to date?

* Will it create more interesting jobs?

* Will it link in with policies around equal opportunities and disability?

* Where are patient needs reflected in the process?

85. Does the new organisation have new training needs?

Mergers are about creating a new organisation with its own new culture and this inevitably means that there will be a variety of training needs across the organisation. Planning and ensuring that there is an agreed training programme is a high priority for success. Merged organisations may not necessarily be composed of 'twinned' organisations; they might be very different, offering quite different services – community and acute services or mental health and community services, as examples. Training in one organisation will be different for another. How will the differing needs be met?

- What training audit should be carried out ?
- Who will carry out an audit and make recommendations?
- What does it reveal and what action does the new board intend to take?
- What is your current training capacity?
- Will you need outside help?
- Is training linked to operational objectives?
- Is training linked to a pay and reward strategy?
- Should it be?
- Is personal development kept separate from organisational and professional development?
- How effective is current training and does it effectively meet needs and develop skills required ?
- What are the resource implications and how will you fund training and development?

86. Do the merging organisations have differing reward strategies ? Can one be adopted or will you have to start from scratch?

Some Trusts may have taken advantage of their freedom to engage staff on pay and conditions determined locally. This may provide a mismatch and differential problems in trying to bring organisations together. A careful review of the reward strategies is essential and the new organisation will need to consider whether any part of these strategies will meet its new needs. It may be decided that a new reward strategy is more appropriate for the future and it will also be important to understand the changing national agenda in this arena. The business plan prepared for the merging organisations has this as a formal requirement.

- Have you reviewed the reward strategies of the merging organisations?
- What are the key differences?
- What elements make sense to keep for the new organisation?
- What will be the consultation process?
- What will be the role of staff organisations?
- What are the cost implications of any changes?
- Will future political changes impact on decisions you may be forced to make in the short term?

87. How will the new board assess future skill-mix requirements?

The skill-mix requirements of the new organisation will need to be carefully considered in the light of its service direction and its priority needs. In all key clinical and care areas it will need to look at its performance and at whether the right levels and standards of care are being delivered, and also at its costs and whether it is delivering value for money. Shifts in treatments from secondary into primary, more sophisticated imaging and diagnostics, short bed-stays and high-tech treatments make skill mix planning a sophisticated task. Managerial functions, formerly manual and in the future likely to be increasingly dependent on technology may mean some staff will see their role drifting beyond their competence. Training and organising work around the needs of the organisation will mean new 'jobs' are invented to meet the delivery mechanisms of the future.

- What is the future direction of the new organisation?
- What are the core service areas?
- Is it currently delivering effective and cost efficient care in these areas?
- If not, why?
- What are the staffing issues?
- How will you review skill mix in these areas?
- How do you compare against good practice elsewhere?
- How attractive are you as an employer?
- What are the technology related skill-mix issues and requirements?

88. Does the service reconfiguration impact on medical manpower and future planning?

Inevitably any mergers of Trusts will impact on the configuration of services and what will be delivered. For the merger to be successful it is essential to involve clinicians throughout the whole process and to gain their support and commitment to the future. It is also important to think more widely about effective use of clinical resources and the potential for using the skills of others.

• What role will clinicians play in the merger process and the reconfiguration of services?

• If the process appears to be spawning more clinical directorates – is this what you want?

• Are clinicians actively involved in decision making or are they an isolated body?

• How involved in policy making is the new medical director?

• Does he/she involve and regularly communicate with other clinicians?

• What is the feedback?

• Is there a key role for former medical directors?

• Does the board and key clinicians have a creative vision for service delivery?

• Are you prepared to develop extended roles for nurse practitioners and other professionals?

• Can computer technology play a greater role in the delivery of clinical care in your new organisation?

89. How will the new organisation assess its IT status?

Good information technology systems are essential to a new organisation, helping it to perform efficiently and in an informed way. The management of information by the use of technology has not been the NHS's strongest suit. However, IT will prove vital in keeping costs down and helping everyone to understand what is going on where they work. Developments in what is available are likely to exceed the NHS's ability to pay for them but electronic patient records, tele-medicine, ward-order systems and pharmacy management systems are just a small part of what is on the horizon.

- What IT systems have you inherited?
- Are they any good?
- Are they Y2K compliant?
- Are they similar and compatible systems?
- Will they meet the needs of the new organisation?
- Who will decide what is needed and how?
- What is the future IT strategy?
- What will it cost and is it affordable?
- What are the plans to develop the use of IT to improve viability?
- Are the systems in place integrated?
- What are the IT capabilities and competencies across the organisation?
- Is there a training and development programme to meet the range of needs?
- Is it affordable?
- Does PFI have a role?
- Are the board of a 'gas-lamp generation' and don't understand its importance?
- What can you do to enthuse them, and train them without making them feel even older?

90. How will the IT agenda be delivered?

Merging organisations may have totally different IT systems and it will be essential to identify the right systems for the new organisation. It may not be relevant to continue to use old systems or to allow duplication. It is a priority to be urgently tackled to enable timely information to be delivered to the board and to staff and to provide the merger project team with reliable information. Merger may be an opportunity for investment in new systems – procurement issues and what the parameters are require great skill and judgment. The IT industry and its commercial offerings are changing and improving at breakneck speed; the right decision today will have a consequence for the organisation tomorrow.

- Is what you have got now up to the job?

- What is the new IT agenda?

- Who will audit current systems?

- What IT systems will the new Trust need to meet its needs?

- Who will help you determine these?

- How will you evaluate you current information status?

- What are the resource implications?

91. Are there changes that need to be made in Chaplaincy or other services?

Organisations merging across territorial boundaries sometimes find themselves spanning new cultures. This is particularly true if patients are likely to be transferred between merging organisations. This can often impact of the range of chaplaincy services or arrangements for the spiritual wellbeing and guidance for staff. Arrangements for relatives at a time of stress and in bereavement might mean the organisation has to make new on-call arrangements for chaplains or other spiritual and community leaders. Perhaps fresh instructions are needed for mortuary arrangements and for laying-out. Some cultures have strict codes and requirements.

- What is the role of the chaplain in the new organisation?

- Where does he/she fit into the managerial hierarchy?

- What review of services is to be undertaken?

- Who shall lead it?

- How can you be sure that the complete range of spiritual requirements is being met?

- Will spiritual and community leaders meet regularly?

- How will it be resourced?

- Will an ecumenical approach be acceptable to patients and their relatives?

- Will 'chapel of rest' arrangements need to be reviewed?

- Will staff need additional training?

- Will new mortuary arrangements be required?

92. The new organisation will need a supplies and purchasing strategy – who will design it?

Efficient supplies and purchasing systems can release significant amounts of cash savings for any new organisation. It will be important to review existing systems and to avoid duplication and confusion. The NHS Supplies Authority are not the only source of supply and the board should be satisfied it is getting the best value for money it can achieve.

- Who will review the current supplies and purchasing arrangements?

- Is the supplies manager an employee of the NHSSA?

- How impartial can they be about supplies performance?

- Is there in-house capacity with creativity to do this?

- If not how will you select and what will it cost?

- Can the Trusts get a better deal by going direct to suppliers?

- How do you assess value for money?

- Do you know?

- How are prices tested?

- Where do you purchase items and why?

- Does the board receive regular bench-marking reports on product comparisons and performance?

- Is everything purchased and delivered according to specification?

- Is there an understood policy on VAT recovery?

- Are all suppliers Y to K compliant?

- Can you prove it?

93. How will the new board agree quality standards?

Awareness of quality issues is reflected in recent decisions to incorporate 'medical quality' issues into Patient Charter standards. Quality does not begin and end with any one department, it is a job for the whole organisation. Setting quality standards involves everyone and requires ownership and commitment. A newly merged organisation will need to agree a new a philosophy and a new shared agenda. It is not acceptable to muddle through with old practices.

- Has the new board defined quality and the standards it expects?

- How different is this from the previous systems?

- How will the new measures form part of the culture of the new organisation?

- What induction and training will there be for all staff?

- Is there a senior person responsible for the overall monitoring of quality?

- Are any audit systems being introduced and if so how?

- How will the board monitor the quality standards and what will come to the board on a regular basis?

- Is there an external assessment of quality?

94. Can the new organisation afford to encourage innovation?

A new organisation must be seen to be open to new ideas and good practice. However it has to be placed in the context of the business direction and affordability as innovation can be expensive and sometimes even risky in terms of success. Clinicians are always anxious to try out new techniques, managers will be keen to try new approaches and staff will want to use the latest and up to date equipment. In the cost constrained environment of the NHS this is impossible. What is possible is the careful targeting of innovation to make the biggest change and improvement possible. Encouraging new ideas without stifling innovation is a careful balance.

- What is the core business direction and is the organisation exposed in any way?

- What are the commissioners' views on innovation and will they set aside funds?

- Will it require cash releasing savings over a period of time to pay back investment in innovation?

- Is it possible?

- Will you want to work with other providers and clinicians in a collaborative way on innovation?

- Is there the potential for partnerships and risk share around innovation with the private sector such as pharmaceutical companies?

95. What is the role of performance management in the existing organisations and what changes will be required in the new?

In all organisations a credible performance management process is required and is also essential for their success. Introducing a fair and accepted system will require vision and a high level of expertise.

- Are there performance monitoring systems in place?

- Is performance development about personal improvement or acquiring technical knowledge?

- Is it both?

- Should it be?

- What are the performance monitoring arrangements in the merging organisations?

- Are they effective ?

- What are the major differences?

- How will a new system to meet the needs of the new organisation be agreed and identified?

- Will it apply across the whole organisation?

- What are its aims?

- Is there the capacity and expertise within to introduce and implement?

- Does the board know what it wants?

- Does personal performance link to corporate goal?

- How?

- How will success be measured?

96. How will the new board manage workload and performance to commissioners' expectations?

It will be essential to work closely and in partnership with your commissioners on workload and performance measures in your contracts and to establish agreements that are meaningful. This is particularly true of a new organisation in the early days of its management. There is a tendency to overperform and out-run resources. Financial controls will play a vital role in satisfying the commissioners and not running out of money in the process.

- Do you have a shared vision with your commissioners for the future of services?

- Do you understand each others' roles?

- Do you have meaningful agreements?

- Are clinicians involved in the process?

- Do you have an agreed process for evaluating performance in sub-services?

- What happens when agreements are out performed before the end of their maturity?

- What are the arrangements for joint discussion and at what level?

- How are disputes settled?

97. How will the new organisation allow the old organisations to grieve their passing?

When developing sound new organisations the evidence would appear to point to the importance of allowing the old organisations and their staff the space and the time to grieve and to reflect on their successes. The equivalent of thanksgiving or celebration services or presentations to outgoing staff, long-serving members and volunteers will help. This can be in the form of formal and informal events with celebrations to commemorate the past and pave the way and welcome the new era. No organisation does everything well and no organisation does everything badly. There is good and bad to be remembered in all things, especially organisations, many of whom will have a long history of public service.

- What will the merger project team do to enable the merging organisations to celebrate their passing and their successes?

- How will these events be chosen, programmed and publicised?

- Who will lead these events?

- What will be the role of the shadow board?

- How will it ensure that there is the time set aside to do this?

- How will the new board ensure that this process of remembering can be continued for an agreed period of time?

- How can this be transformed into focusing energy on developing and nurturing the new culture and the new organisation?

- What will be the new role of the chief executive?

98. How will you develop a checklist to see if the merger is working?

It is easy for merger paralysis to set in and for those preoccupied with delivering the merger agenda to develop tunnel vision. It will be very important to set up checks and balances and to include an independent voice to ensure that the agreed vision is being delivered and mistakes along the way are quickly remedied and learnt from.

- Who will be responsible for evaluating the merger process along the way?
- How will you ensure that they are listened to?
- What checks and balances will be set up?
- How will the checklist be set up?
- Who will ensure that changes are made and mistakes heeded?
- Will you use the services of an independent adviser?
- How will you select?
- How will it be reported back to both the board and the staff?
- How will it fit in with your communications strategy?

99. Was the merger worth it?

Mergers and reconfigurations should only be embarked on if there is clarity about what the benefits are. There must also be the top teams with the skills and energy to take on this difficult task without damaging the performance of key service delivery. Where organisations are already under-performing in key areas, lack capacity and where boards are not keen supporters then it is often not desirable or worth it. Merger mania can create unrealistic optimism and merger myopia can take over as an end in itself – rather than looking ahead to the future.

Two turkeys don't make an eagle!

- What key diagnosis was done at the pre-merger stage?
- Was there clarity around the benefits that the merger should deliver?
- Did it?
- Were the organisational cultures understood and differences identified?
- Was an appropriate change management strategy chosen and agreed?
- Did it work?
- Was the nature of the reconfiguration and whether it was a merger or an acquisition clearly understood?
- Have the pitfalls been identified?
- Was there the capacity to deliver the agreed merger agenda?
- Were the right leaders selected with the right skills?
- How effective was communication and consultation?
- How effective has the process been?
- Has it been worth it?
- Can you pass on your lessons?

100. How will the board know if the new organisation is a good place to live, work, be treated and cared for?

A newly merged organisation will have a new board which must successfully translate the aims of the new organisation into a real vision and with a new culture, with values that are supported, agreed and understood by its staff. This means creating an environment which staff are proud of and services which local people trust and believe in.

- How will the board develop a new culture?
- What will be the key steps?
- Who will lead it?
- How will it engage with staff?
- How will the agenda be implemented?
- How inclusive can you make the key decision-making processes?
- How will the board know that it is moving in the right direction?
- Who will it listen to?
- How will it monitor its own actions as well as the performance of others?
- What is the organisation's barometer?
- How accessible does the new board plan to be?
- How will it know it has succeeded?

101. What will you tell the others?

We wrote a book about our *merger experience* and tried to pass on the pleasure, the pain, the sense of achievement at a job well done and the disappointments. What will you do? People will want to hear from you, about how it felt, the mistakes you made, and what you would do again. Sharing knowledge. How will you do it?

- Will you speak at conferences?
- Will you write a book?
- Will you have an open door for those who want to learn from you?
- Will you tell the truth?
- How will we know?

Appendix A: Seven Golden Rules for Mergers

1. Gossip and speculation about the possibility of merger can set the tone for the whole process. So, move like greased lightning. Tell everyone as fast as you can that discussions are going on and keep them bang up-to-date with the outcomes.

2. Be honest about why the merger is to take place. Don't pretend it is about better service if the real task is to save money. People aren't daft.

3. Get a handle on the size of the task and be realistic about time-scales. What are you asking managers to do? Is it realistic?

4. Be straight with staff about their futures. If some are to go, help them move on if you can. People have families, mortgages and bills to pay. You can't begin to understand morale and motivation until you understand that.

5. The project team must be properly resourced and not weighed down with day-to-day responsibilities as well as merge duties. Help them become a team.

6. Don't use the word communicate! Do it! Talk to people, write them, go and see them and do as much as you can face to face. Explain what is going on and why and share with people your vision of what the new organisation will look like.

7. Respect the past and take the best of it into the future.

Appendix B:
What Other People Said about Mergers

As this book was being written Nexus Structured Communications of Guildford, Surrey, together with the weekly magazine for health service managers, The Health Service Journal, *published the results of an in-depth poll of senior managers called 'Trust Mergers'. With their kind permission we republish some of the comments from the survey, together with extracts from the data. The comments are incisive and instructive, from CEOs and others who are contemplating merger, have experienced merger or who are likely to be forced into the merger process.*

The results of the survey struck a resonance with the authors of this book and underpins many of their thoughts and reflections.

Mergers will only be effective if driven by services. If it is about other reasons, eg yet more organisational change, then it will neither benefit patients nor reduce costs.

Mergers must be linked to agreed local health strategies and be based upon improving the case process associated with patients.

Mergers should only occur when the driving force is service improvement – a principle which is markedly absent in most cases. Each case should be considered on its merit (but isn't). If there was a clear vision of the desired outcome from mergers there would be an emerging pattern discernible – there is not. Financial crisis, dogma and personal ambition seem to be the main driving forces – not very evidently a focus on patient care.

I consider that combined Trusts are the most appropriate model and therefore have a view that community Trusts may be absorbed.

There are mergers that will work because the parties involved will be natural partners, but those that are just mergers for mergers sake will prove very painful for all concerned.

They can be extremely beneficial in bringing skilled management into small organisations that did not either have the resources to recruit to this level or, perhaps, the vision to see what they needed. Very small trusts merge to form slightly bigger, more robust organisations that can see these needs.

Mergers may save some non-exec's salaries but generally speaking significant amounts of cash will not be released. This is an opinion I hold and is not based upon research other than reading a few articles about some mergers which have taken place.

They appear often to be short-sighted, politically led with a view to achieving short-term management savings, without any consideration of management effectiveness.

The merger process itself consumes huge resources and diverts senior staff attention from operational issues. We don't seem capable of learning lessons from the private sector. Has anyone heard of opportunity costs? I can believe the lack of realism about savings and costs of change.

There should be proper consideration given to the NHS structure of the future – mergers (if any) should then be planned in the light of that. Fiddling about at the margins should be avoided. Pros and cons of the different arrangements should be properly addressed before changes are formally made.

Change is driven by politics, not common sense. At a time when 'small is beautiful and responsive' why return to large lumbering remote organisations? Where is the evidence that larger organisations deliver most effective/more efficient services?

It is essential to ensure that some very clear service principles are established before any merger is contemplated.

The first casualty of merger is truth.

There is possibly an optimal size for trusts and clearly some are too small, but the idea that mergers will produce significant management cost savings has not been demonstrated. Real drivers for mergers have little to do with costs of patient care, and more to do with political pressures, local and national.

While mergers are likely to reduce 'countable' management costs, the knock-on effect of extended internal lines of communication on the efficiency of the organisation will mitigate against overall savings. Mergers should be justified on service benefits (including any real resources released). This does not often seem to be the prime objective.

Having been involved in the management of two ambulance mergers, I believe there are benefits to the parties and the service particularly in relation to ambulance service. The process is complex and must be driven in a positive manner (seems obvious but not always central to thoughts).

History shows that whenever faced with a crisis or major problem the NHS seeks to re-organise rather than tackle the underlying problem!

Mergers can only be successful if trusts have sufficient senior skilled managers to implement them. I doubt whether many have such.

It is very rare that the benefits outweigh the opportunity cost. It is a smoke screen by the politicians to hide real service problems.

It is essential in my view that service reconfiguration precedes organisational merger. Reconfiguration should be service led and not finance driven.

The current programme for trust reconfiguration in Wales will provide an opportunity to improve problems raised by trust establishments.

If merger is the answer – what was the question?

Must be service rather than financially driven (if you are to take staff with you).

Mergers are an outdated way of dealing with change. Rather than change the business unit, service alliances should be built up – administrative structures can follow.

A great destruction of management time and energy not addressing real resource issues in healthcare. My strong view is that some trusts should get smaller not larger and therefore closer to patients and their communities, and with that, more efficient use of resources, although this is not necessarily the case in acute trusts.

The merger proposals appear driven by region and purchasers without there being any proper appraisal of the costs and benefits. This seems based on the assumption that relatively small savings in management and administration costs are more important than assessing potential synergies in delivery of patient services. Similarly the provision of funding for transitional costs in setting up the merger of trusts is being ignored.

Mergers alone will not bring savings or improvements in patient care. An operational match of strengths and weaknesses must give rise to a merger, combined with effective management to exploit the advantages.

Having already undergone a merger of two DMUs (directly managed units) to create a trust, we found that mergers will divert the organisation's attention from real patient orientated issues to unproductive management organisational issues for the next two years.

Everybody is calculating the costs of management savings but nobody wants to tackle the issue of making clinicians redundant or reskilling/reprofiling the medical workforce; this is where there are huge savings to be had.

If you want to get rid of the Tories on quangos, there must be easier ways. If there's no more money, why won't Health Authorities accept their role and tell the public that they've got to ration services?

Most senior managers wish they were 50 – so they can have more options.

I believe the current drive for mergers is driven by political dogma. Health and Social Services will suffer, if a policy on mergers is pursued at an inappropriate speed and without the necessary consultation, research and analysis.

We are not planning to merge with another Trust, but we are involved in a major collaboration with two other Trusts and two health authorities to plan the future disposition of services in our area.

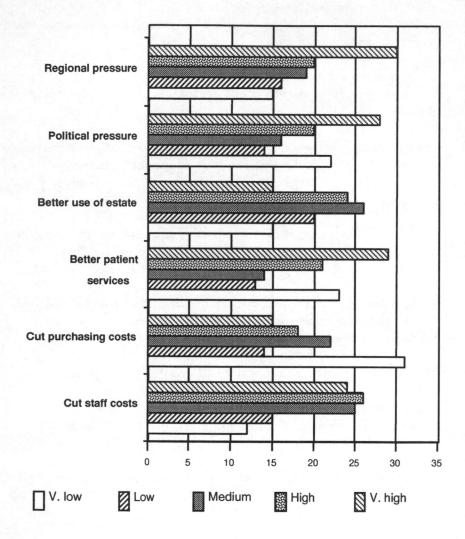

Figure 1 Motivators to merge

Source Nexus Structured Communications/*The Health Service Journal*

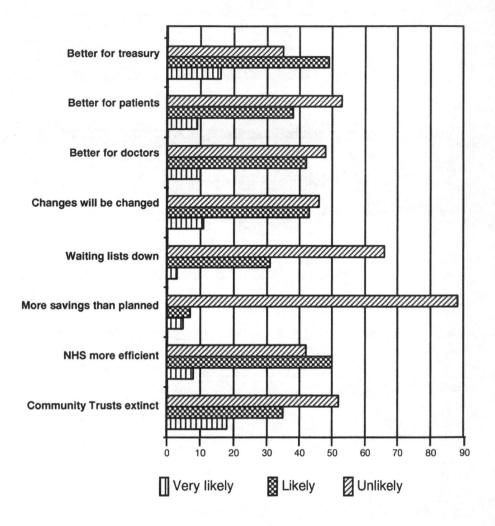

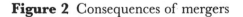

Figure 2 Consequences of mergers

Source Nexus Structured Communications/ *The Health Service Journal*

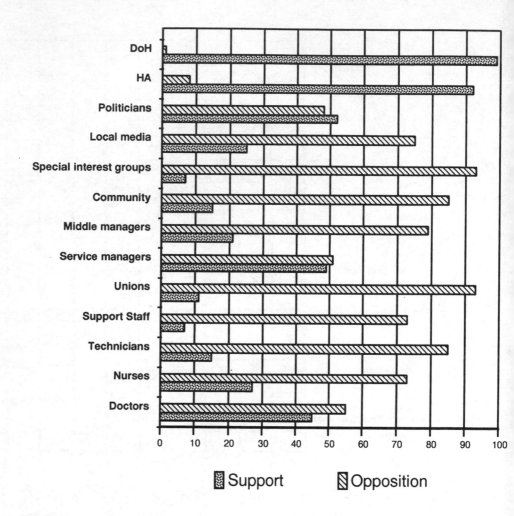

Figure 3 Where will the support/opposition come from?

Source Nexus Structured Communications/*The Health Service Journal*

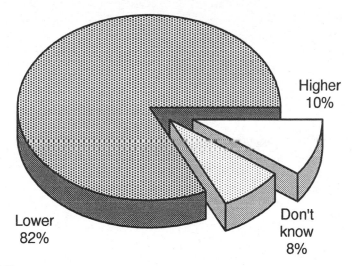

Figure 4 Effect on morale

Source Nexus Structured Communications/ *The Health Service Journal*

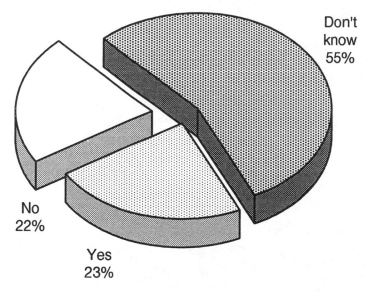
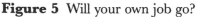

Figure 5 Will your own job go?

Source Nexus Structured Communications/ *The Health Service Journal*

INDEX